D1616218

BUILDING *SEX*

BUILDING *SEX*

Men, Women, Architecture, and the Construction of Sexuality

AARON BETSKY

WILLIAM MORROW AND COMPANY, INC. NEW YORK

Illustration Credits, constituting a continuation of the copyright
page, begin on page 226.

It is the policy of William Morrow and Company, Inc., and its
imprints and affiliates, recognizing the importance of preserving
what has been written, to print the books we publish on acid-free
paper, and we exert our best efforts to that end.

Library of Congress Cataloging-in-Publication Data

Betsky, Aaron.
Building sex : men, women, architecture, and the construction of
sexuality / Aaron Betsky. — 1st ed.
p.   cm.
Includes bibliographical references and index.

ISBN 0–688–13167–0
1. Architecture and women.   2. Architecture and society.
I. Title.
NA2543.W65B48   1995
720´.1´03—dc20   94–34019 CIP

Printed in the United States of America

 2 3 4 5 6 7 8 9 10

BOOK DESIGN BY ADAMS/MORIOKA

to my mother
_____

Acknowledgments

This book is ultimately the result of the faith of John Meunier, who, as director of the Department of Architecture at the University of Cincinnati, hired me fresh out of school in 1983 to teach courses in interior design. He supported my efforts to rewrite the history and theory of that discipline as an attempt by women to make a place of their own within a male-dominated environment. As I developed courses in this area, Celia McGee was my guide, mentor, and supporter. Catherine Lynn, T. J. Jackson Lears, Jeffrey Meikle, Harvey Green, and Richard Guy Wilson were among those who helped guide the project.

Almost ten years later Lisa Queen provoked me to revisit that research and extend it through the use of more current scholarship by asking the question that begins this book. Ann Bergren, Sarah Betsky-Zweig, and Kevin McMahon were of great help in this effort, pointing the way to some of the central texts that I hope inform this book. Diana Solway, David Resnicow, Betsy Amster, Angela Miller, and my editor, Paul Bresnick, also were invaluable in guiding the project.

Finally, I would not have been able to complete this project without the support of Peter Christian Haberkorn and the indefatigable research efforts of An Te Liu.

Contents

ix

Figure I.1: Jean-Charles Geslin, *La Place de la Concorde*, 1846

"WHY DO I ALWAYS FEEL OUT OF PLACE when I'm walking down the Champs-Élysées?" a woman asked me when I was waxing enthusiastic about the grandeur of Paris. "Because you are a woman," I responded. The Champs-Élysées, I went on to explain, was designed by men. It represents their power. You might even say that it represents the body of a man. The street starts in front of a very large building (the Louvre) that has two legs reaching out to the street. At the center of each leg is a slightly higher portion that corresponds to the breast. It is rigid and symmetrical, muscular, and festooned with columns. The combination of the geometry, the phallic imagery, and the way in which the building looks like a man in granite armor is intimidating and is meant to be so.

The whole building dominates a large court. It sends out a long line that is the Champs-Élysées. It was constructed with little regard for what had been on the site; it was an erection, symbolized by the obelisk that stands at the beginning of the street. Where the Champs-Élysées ends, it marks its triumph with an arch and a round plaza that sends out many smaller avenues like so many nearly identical but smaller children disseminated across the field of Paris.

Figure I.2: The Champs-Élysées toward the Arc de Triomphe, Paris

xi

Figure I.3:
Tuileries Gardens, Paris

where, from the phallic constructions of skyscrapers to the "muscular" constructions of our civic buildings. Men rule, and their power is made real through architecture.

Yet women have their revenge. Nobody really cares about architecture. Most people don't even notice the shapes over which architects slaved so much. A building has to be pretty large or strange (like the Louvre or the Sears Tower) to make us realize that it is even there. The world that men have made, the world of the straight streets, proud erections, and rational relationships that make up our cities, is not very popular. Most of us see our world as alien, uncomfortable, and even dangerous. We want to go to shopping malls, to parks, and into our homes. In our society these are the realms of women.

A shopping mall, for instance, is usually not a piece of "good" architecture. It is a blob that contains riches. It has no facade, and it does not propagate anything except entrance signs. Inside, the route you take is often serpentine. It has few edges and seems to be woven together out of all the merchandise on display. Space dissolves; textures emerge. This is a world that we think of as feminine. It is a place where we can delight in

On either side of the oldest part of the street were parks. These were places where nature was rebuilt in a domesticated version. Here grand purpose gave way to sensual but contained delights. You could lose yourself within the geometry, rather than be confronted with it as an image. Trees spread their leaves, light was filtered, and a collage of paths and levels made you lose yourself as if in a labyrinth. Here culture reigned, people drifted in and out, wares were once sold, and men could find prostitutes. This was the place of women.

You can "read" the whole situation as a picture of the relationship between men and women in our society. Men dominate space, and women are shunted to the side to sex, nature, and culture. Male body imagery is every-

what we have made, where real and fantasy mix, where we go to clothe ourselves. It is a place of activities and qualities that, for some reason, in our society are seen as feminine. The shopping mall has become the female temple.

A woman's "real" place, of course, is the home. That is where she cooks, cleans, and takes care of the children. A house might look like something on the outside (though these days our fear of violence is making houses increasingly into just blank boxes), but it is the inside that matters. The most popular image of a dream home is of a rambling, expansive set of rooms, each one connected to another. Their shapes are defined either by use or by such comfort factors as light and air. A dining room should be near the kitchen but also near the living room. It should be large enough to house guests but not too large to overwhelm the family. The table should be well lighted, the chairs should be comfortable, and the whole place should be conducive to conversation.

We fill our houses with objects of memory: photographs, paintings, and mementos. We cover them with fabrics and stake out areas in them with rugs, beds, chairs, and lights. Unless we have decorators, our homes are usually a mess, at least if you try to judge them by the criteria of orderliness we use in looking at the outside world. We feel at home there. We go out only because we have to, unless we are going to another place of pleasure or culture.

This is not something new. Behind the facades that line the Champs-Élysées, women made their salons. Marked by asymmetrical designs and sensual materials, these were sheltered places of culture where the orders made outside there by men could be criticized, evaluated, and domesticated. Women had a role and a place: to make livable the world men made.

We thus live in a strangely and unequally divided world. Our man-made world was made by men. Men founded our cities and designed the buildings in them. Men decided what the world we travel through every day was going to look like, and men decided what the streets would look like. Men planned, designed, built, and ran the towns, suburbs, and cities we live in. Where were women during all this? They were the ones who made this world livable. They made the homes comfortable and the streets places of activity. Women brought up the children and cared for the old. They made the grand plans of

Figure I.4: Edmond Marmion, An English Lady's Bedchamber, c. 1640

xiii

Figure I.5: Thomas Cole, The Architect's Dream, 1840

Figure I.6:
Le Corbusier,
Plan Voisin, Paris,
1925

men real within a framework that contained and imprisoned them.

The result has been a split in the world we inhabit. Men rule the outside, women the inside. On the one hand, there are the grand structures of men. They are impressive palaces, skyscrapers, and straight streets. They are cold, oppressive, and inhuman. Then there is the interior realm women have carved out within this world. It is warm, sheltering, rich, and comfortable. We are taught that we should aspire to the world of men, which is a world of importance and meaning, but we feel at home in the world created by women.

This distinction is obviously absurd. There is no reason why skyscrapers are more important than bedrooms or why women should make places that are more comfortable than those men make. Our culture has assigned these roles and made these places, building on the skills and attributes of our bodies but transforming them into roles that are as oppressive as those we ascribe to wage earners, soldiers, or prostitutes.

The rule of men came first. In a culture dominated by men, it was assumed that men should build and women should decorate. Men were actors in the public realm, while women were passive recipients of their largess. This was so, men thought, because it was decreed in the Bible, because woman was by her nature sinful, or because these roles were biologically determined. After all, women have wombs and men have penises; ergo, women protect and men project. This strange conflation of biological form and social roles goes almost unquestioned to this day. Writers who want to prove that this makes women superior have even given it a feminist twist.

The split between projection and protection is not a fact of nature. It is a fact of man. It is the result of millennia of oppression of women by men. It has resulted in a world of inhuman cities in which we try to carve out places for ourselves. That means that we all are women trying to make ourselves at home in a world of men. It means that we all inhabit two worlds: one of projection that is artificial, abstract, and male; the other of protection that is sensual, informal, and female.

How did this situation come into being? This book will trace a journey in time and place from a world of nomadic tribes to the stratified world of agriculture, through the erection of male boundaries and territories and the emergence of female realms, through the isolation of the world of women within an ever-larger world of men, to the gradual recapture and dis-solution of that world that started in the nineteenth century and continues to this day. In the end, I shall claim, we can and must make a world of and for men and women and all those beings whose gender we cannot and should not define.

I shall not argue about the "natural" place of men and women. Several recent critics have said that the divi-sion between the sexes starts in the womb, where women shelter their babies in the prototype of an interior. All the homes women then make in the world are attempts to rebuild that realm for their infants. Female chil-dren copy this activity when they grow up. Men, for some reason that must be hard-wired into their brain (or, and

this is the one place where feminists agree with Freud, because they have penises that project out urine and semen), leave these homes and desire their spaces as images of their mothers. They build homes that are versions of themselves to attract women to them and then allow these women to shelter inside. They go out and find resources for the women, defend them, and protect them. They

Figure I.7:
View of Midtown Manhattan,
c. 1931

also keep the women, who just want to procreate as much as possible and are thus by nature promiscuous, inside so that they can't get at other men.

This, we are still told, is natural. It is just the way things are. The woman is a virgin and a whore because that is what her body "tells her" to be. Evidence from everything like how male apes shelter females to the behavior of New Guinea natives to the games little children play is used as evidence of the inevitable, natural fact of projection and protection. The big feminist twist is to reverse the usual value judgment about this "fact": Females, these new apologists argue, are in touch with the rhythms and laws of nature because they ovulate and give birth. Men are not, and thus they create an artificial alternative to this world. It is fake, but it is our culture. We should accept the fact that men made our culture and that they made it evil because the very act of suppressing nature is evil. What makes the world of literature, art, and music vital, they say, is the danger or reality of a female nature that always threatens to pervert, to seduce, or even to destroy the clear-cut alternative structure men have created. Thus high art is decadent and delicious, more real and more sensuous than abstract male work. It is the woman's revenge against male order.

I shall leave it to anthropologists to continue their work in figuring out whether these assigned roles are facts. I shall merely point out that these are all interpretations that we lay over observations. The very fact that we go looking for reasons to explain the division between the sexes is a product of our culture. We want to assign roles and tasks and create a truth. We assume that a house should be like our body. We assume that a grid we project over a landscape should be like urine. Somehow, we assume, our brain makes that connection.

Let's look at it the other way around. A house is not a body. Urine is not a street. Why do we make the connection? How do we construct these analogies? What purpose do they serve? The single answer to these questions is that they help us find our way in the world. What is more important, they divide power and resources. They assign qualities and allow us to judge our reality. If a building is like a body, it should have a front, a back, a bottom, a middle, and a top. It should have legs and a face (or facade). If "projection" is a male act, that means we can efficiently ascribe that task to a certain group. Women will stay in their place or, if the feminists "win," will destroy male structures and replace them with female cohousing. In either case, people will know their places and make them.

I should like to question these orders by tracing the history of these connections. I shall present the various arguments for the space of women and men and survey the evidence out of which these separate spaces have been constructed. I shall not pass judgment on whether this is a true connection or not but merely tell the story of a history of separation, in which men assigned a separate space to women and then constructed an architecture of wood, stones, and justifications that formalized those separate realms. I shall not argue for more power for women or a different role but merely question whether we need this elaborate architecture. Why do we need to have separate spaces? Why do we need architecture?

I am here speaking about the artificial construct of gender, though I am not sure we can really separate these values from the various biological attributes we associate with men and women. I am talking not about the "facts" of men and women but about what we make out of them and how we use them to make places for ourselves in the world. I shall argue that in fact, architecture in its broadest sense is how we construct our sexualities in the real world and thus define ourselves in a given place and time.

This book is about Western culture. It does not trace the slightly different realms assigned to women by men in other cultures, except by comparison. My story begins at the dawn of what we think of as our civilization but only speculates on the spaces of women until the Middle Ages. There is a philosophical issue at stake here, though, that goes back in time before the building of temples or homes.

Culture is the product of making a place. It is only when a species settles down in one particular part of the space of the world and, using tools and language, makes it into a place with boundaries, routes, directions, and dimensions that it constructs a world. Space becomes a place through architecture, and we define ourselves within a certain time and place. We define the space in which we appear, and that act of appearance then defines our roles in society.

In our society the allocation of space and roles seems pretty fixed. For that reason I am fascinated by nomadic cultures. They seem to exist between space and place. Cultures like that of the Australian Aborigines trace lines of connection in the sand that are soon wiped clean by the wind. They create structures out of natural materials that either become part of the baggage they carry with them or are abandoned before new ones are constructed. They do not claim a

Figure I.8:
Édouard Vuillard,
*Interior of the Library of
Dr. Vaquez: The Reader,*
c. 1896

tural theoreticians like to think that it all started when Adam made a home for Eve in paradise or when some unknown man made a house that gave shelter and mimicked the four directions of the winds, the trees or mountains out of which it was made, or the male body. This male construction stands in contrast with the cave, the natural womb out of which man set forth in his quest to conquer the world.

I propose another model: the hut or tepee, woven together by men and women together (though each may have a separate task). It is round, omnidirectional, and flexible. It can be added on to, and it can be demounted. It is somewhere between the cave and the construction, somewhere between a woven cloth put down on the ground and something with walls and a roof. It allows us to be at home in the world.

In many ways we are returning to the world of nomads. Few of us occupy one place, one house, or one job for very long. The average American moves once every other year, for instance. We try to navigate through a man-made world that has become as large and complex as the natural world must have seemed to the first wanderers. We stake a claim to that world by

place but occupy it in a provisional manner. They tell stories about why they are on this earth that do not distinguish between the real and the imaginary, between gods and humans, or between the constructions of man and the structures of nature. They live outside fixed boundaries and laws. Theirs is a mutable world woven together by the textures of language, art, and common agreement.

This is my ideal. It is what I shall call our first home in the world. Architec-

redecorating homes, apartments, or offices that we accept as natural facts, rather than build them for ourselves. We make our own provisional additions, unpacking our belongings piece by piece, memento by memento, book by book, until they cover every surface, change the structures we inhabit, take over more territory, and then, more often than not, we move on.

Who makes these nomadic moments? Men and women together. Are they architecture or interiors, buildings or baggage? It is difficult to say. Partially planned and partially the result of sensual needs, they are, above all else, sensible. In this way we make ourselves at home in the world.

This is not necessarily a bad way to live, except that we feel as if we have to claim or privatize little pieces of an alien environment to accomplish this. We also don't value this activity because we have been taught that permanence and order are the building blocks of society. We *should,* I shall argue, dream of weaving together a realm of men and women. We can imagine a world in which interior and exterior flow together, structure dissolves into surface, comfort and abstractions are intertwined. It would be an extension of the small moments of coherence we make every day

for ourselves, but it would include others. It would mean a breakdown of law and order and the making of another place.

In a way, this dream stands for a world without men and women, at least as we know them, just as it stands for a world without classes or races and perhaps even a world without human beings. It is a dream that is neither one in which we dissolve back into (feminine) nature nor one in which we continue to build (male) alternatives, but a world where we fold ourselves into a texture of culture, a landscape that gives birth to many different sexes and forms.

This is a nice reverie. In reality, we first need to trace the emergence of the prisons of femininity and the facades of masculinity in order to question them. If we can merely not be so sure about how we are constructed, if we can understand that it is not inevitable that we wander down the mean streets or retreat into our defensible private realms, we can already start to build another sex.

xix

1

OF PENISES AND TENTS

IN THE EARLY 1950S THE PSYCHIATRIST ERIK ERIKSON conducted a series of experiments in Berkeley, California. He asked young boys and girls (just before puberty) to construct "exciting movie sets" out of building blocks. The results, he reported, showed a remarkable difference between the dreamworlds of the two sexes:

> The girl's scene is an interior scene, represented either as a configuration of furniture without any surrounding walls, or by a simple enclosure built with blocks. In the girl's scene, people and animals are mostly within such an interior or enclosure, and they are primarily people or animals in a static (sitting, standing) position. Girls' enclosures consist of low walls, i.e., only one block high, except for an occasional doorway. These interiors of houses with or without walls were, for the most part, expressively peaceful. Often, a little girl was playing a piano. In a number of cases, however, the interior was intruded by animals or dangerous men. Yet the idea of an intruding creature did not necessarily lead to the defensive erection of walls or the closing of doors. Rather the majority of these intrusions have an element of humor and of pleasurable excitement.

> Boys' scenes are either houses with elaborate walls or facades with protrusions such as cones or cylinders representing ornaments or cannons. There are high towers; and there are exterior scenes. In boys' construc-

tions more people and animals are outside enclosures or buildings, and there are more automotive objects and animals moving along streets and intersections. There are elaborate automotive accidents, but also traffic channeled or arrested by the policeman. While high structures are prevalent in the configuration of boys, there is also much play with danger of collapse or downfall; ruins were exclusively boys' constructions.

These space preferences, Erikson claimed, paralleled the shapes of sexual organs: "[I]n the male, an external organ, erectible and intrusive in character, serving the channelization of mobile sperm cells; internal organs in the female, with vestibular access, leading to statically expectant ova."[1]

The experiments, he said, confirmed what we would expect to find just because of the difference in the makeup of men's and women's bodies. Following standard Freudian doctrine, Erikson pointed out that each woman shelters an interior world in her body (the womb) and thus replicates this activity in the real world. A man, on the other hand, has no such space. To him, birth, nurture, and protection are alien qualities. He does, however, have a penis. This appendage sticks out into space and extends its reach even farther through urination or ejaculation. The woman only has a "wound" where she (according to male psychoanalysts) desires to have such an appendage. Women thus feel a lack, for which they compensate by seeking to fill their void.[2]

The architecture of the body would thus seem to determine not just what we look like but how we behave and, ultimately, our place in the world. This argument has been the bedrock of all sexual divisions in our society. The woman's body is an inside that nurtures and protects. It is like a house, and therefore, women stay at home. A man's body is a weapon, a coupling device, an object that completes itself outside itself. It is a temple. It projects its symmetrical, vertical orders over the world and impregnates.

Psychoanalytic thinkers since Freud have extended this line of thinking by pointing out that the child bonds with the mother but must learn how to separate him- or herself. For the boy, that means that he defines himself by identifying with something outside the maternal embrace—namely, the father—and with this separation, this moving outward, a whole chain of events starts. It leads the boy outward to play, to define, to master his world and to dominate women. It makes the boy the architect of the world he surveys. His architecture is one of separation, difference, and definition.

The girl, on the other hand, grows through identification, taking on the characteristics of her mother and extending the process of identification by playing with dolls.[3] She grows by filling out what she already is, within a known universe. She reweaves the relationship with her mother into bonds with friends and objects, creating an artificial womb around her. Her architecture moves out in concentric, continuous circles. The girl stays at home and makes a domestic universe. In this sense, the real world we all inhabit is no more than a mirror of the architecture of the sexes. Women's domestic role is determined by biology. To many observers, there is even a relationship between the way women appear as the result of their different roles in child rearing that determines their literal place in the world. As no less an authority than Martin Luther put it, "Men have broad shoulders and narrow hips, and accordingly they possess intelligence. Women have narrow shoulders and broad hips. Women ought to stay at home; the way they were created indicates this, for they have broad hips and a wide fundament to sit upon."[4]

This is a powerful argument. It has been extended by thinkers into much more speculative realms. Camille Paglia, for instance, argues that we associate women with nature because they give birth and nurture. To her the feminine is the "chthonic," the wild world of natural forces that men replace with an artificial, man-made world. The feminine or chthonic, however, continually has its revenge, perverting and eventually killing off man and all his sophisticated constructions.[5] In a sense this argument is nothing new. The identification of the feminine with the natural and the male with the artificial dates back at least to the Greeks.[6]

In these arguments there is a male architecture that is a necessary response to the need of the man to separate himself from his mother and define his own world. That architecture in turn shelters his wife, who will become the next mother. The relationship between the cyclical, recurrent world of childbearing and the linear thrust of the creation of new worlds defines much art, architecture, and literature. Some have even claimed that it is the ur-text for all great narratives.[7]

We have to remember, however, that it is just that, a text. It is an attempt to explain not the reality of what it means to be a man or a woman but what we become as men and women in a society, or how we build a society by defining men and women. Simone de Beauvoir, for instance, is probably the most sensitive chronicler of the way in which the different relationship of boy and girl to mother determines one's social and spatial path through life. In *The Second Sex* she is careful to point out that:

> a society is not a species, for it is in society that the species attains the status of existence—transcending itself toward the world and toward the future. Its ways and customs cannot be deduced from biology, for the individuals that compose the society are never abandoned to the dictates of their nature; they are subject rather to that second nature which is custom and which has always reflected the desires and the fears that express their essential nature. It is not merely as a body, but rather as a body subject to taboos, to laws, that the subject is conscious of himself and attains fulfillment—it is with reference to certain values that he evaluates himself.[8]

Ultimately what we would do if we were all alone in the world, without appearing in any society, is unknowable. We know ourselves only through the way we appear and through the constructions in which we appear. The simple act of nurturing extends into a complicated environment we call a home, which we make not just out of walls and beds and kitchens but out of laws and conventions as well. Within that complicated construct the woman has been reduced to one role—namely, to take care of reproduction. We have taken the logic of reproduction and erected over it a world of production, in which men and women have different places and functions. This is a very efficient division; it is one of the foundations of a smoothly working economy. It also causes much pain through the very act of separation and is oppressive in its results.

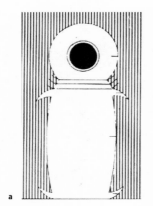

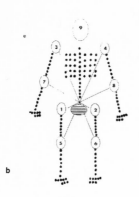

There is a logic to this construction, of course. Education is the next step after nurturing, and taking care of the home is a continuation of taking care of children. Going out into the world in a job in a gridded skyscraper is just an extension of what the man does in this allocation of reproductive roles. In fact, the difficulty often faced by feminist critics is that they have to explain away this logic.

What is not logical is the way we accept this situation as the only possible outcome for any society. It is a far way from the act of giving birth to the enclosure of women in a world made by men, yet we rarely question this development. The results are so profoundly alienating that I believe that we cannot accept them. The home has become a prison that frames women in constructs made by men, while men in turn are trapped in their own artificial worlds, often unable to enter into the physical relationships nurtured within the home.

Let's put it this way: Our bodies are what we make out of them. On the facts of biology, we erect a complicated architecture in which we appear and act as men and women, and each has his or her own place. Aside from the fact that recent medical science has made it clear that the boundaries between the sexes are not always that easy to draw, we have also come to realize that our gender is an artificial construct. We choose how to follow the dictates of nature, or we follow them in a particular manner. We make ourselves as men or women as we make ourselves as human beings, by separating ourselves off from nature, defining ourselves as something that is not the world but like other human beings, and then constructing a world for ourselves. We have done this as a race since the beginning of human consciousness, and we continue to do it as each one of us opens his or her eyes at birth. As we confront the world, we shape ourselves and we shape it. Because of the peculiar relationship between our societies and our bodies, the nature of that shaping takes on very different contours for men and women.

That shape has qualities that already prefigure where we will find ourselves later in life. According to de Beauvoir, the associations go back even before the act of childbirth to the egg itself:

The term "female" is derogatory not because it emphasizes woman's ani-mality, but because it imprisons her in her sex; and if this sex seems to man to be contemptible and inimical even in harmless dumb animals, it is evidently because of the uneasy hostility stirred up in him by woman. Nevertheless he wishes to find in biology a justification for this sentiment. The word *female* brings up in his mind a saraband of imagery—a vast, round ovum engulfs and castrates the agile spermatozoon; the monstrous and swollen termite queen rules over the enslaved males; the female pray-ing mantis and the spider, satiated with love, crush and devour their part-ners; the bitch in heat runs through the alleys, trailing behind her a wake of depraved odors; the she-monkey presents her posterior immodestly and then steals away with hypocritical coquetry. . . .[9]

There is, of course, no biological fact for this kind of imagery. The egg and the sperm do not behave in ways we do in human society. We merely erect a construct of interpretation that allows us to make sense out of our reproduc-tive processes.

Attempts to ground the division between the sexes in biology by looking at the behavior of apes or even other mammals have similarly produced nothing but contradictory results. As Donna Haraway has pointed out, the whole notion of a scientifically defined male and female behavior pattern is as much created by science as it is discov-ered.[10] There is nothing that says that males are always more aggres-sive, more given to use tools, or the

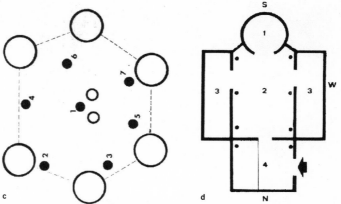

Figure 1.1: Anthropomorphic Diagrams: a) Fali, Granary of the *Ma* Type, Cameroon; b) Dogon Cosmic Diagram, Mali; c) Fali, Domestic Enclosure, Cameroon; d) Dogon Plan of Family House, Mali

creators of constructs that we merely translate into built form.[11] What is most important, males often are not the ones with power. In fact, it turns out that power is a human construct that may have its roots in the first differentiation between men and women.

Figure 1.2: Aboriginal Campfire, from Louis de Freycinet, *Voyage Autour du Monde*, 1824–1844

Ultimately we cannot know what the "real" relationships are between our bodies and our selves. We can know only how we appear and how these relationships play themselves out in human society. What we can know is those appearances, which make up the architecture of the man-made world. In order to sort out these difficult issues, I would like to engage in a little speculative history. The aim is to find out why we have ended up living in a man-made world. The only thing we know for a fact is that in our species women give birth and nurture, and men do not. That does not mean that one is better than the other or that males are destined to act in a certain way and women in another. It merely means that in the beginning women suckled their young.

The first act of building a human culture that sets us apart from animals is the campfire. Whether it is fire that made us human, as the Greeks believed, or the acquisition of language through communal discussion, which is the commonplace foundation myth among anthropologists and cultural historians, it is the gathering of a group of men and women around a campfire, speaking and making things, that makes a place, a community, and social relations. The campground fixes in time, place, language, and eventually custom those things that make real to us whatever mysterious processes make us conscious. It all comes out into the open in the campground, a place that has to be made through communal effort and around which stories are told, tools are made, relationships and clothes are woven. The campground is the first architecture of human culture, and it is how we define ourselves.

The campground is a place that has certain interesting spatial characteristics. It is, of course, generally round. It is not a building but a spot in the ground, usually chosen because it is sheltered by characteristics of the natural landscape, such as rocks. It is a level place around which a group can gather. It gains its strength from the fire, which is an artificial creation that allows for many other artificial acts: cooking, drying and curing, eventually even smelting. The foundation of human culture is a porous circle marked out in the landscape that turns the continuum of nature into a place where artifacts are created. We still commemorate the first campground in the sacred symbol of the mandala, a circle that sums up and transforms nature into a human world.

It is also important to point out what the campground is not. It is horizontal, not vertical. It is neither a womb nor a projection, but a place of gathering and definition. It is not hierarchical, and it is difficult to define as a separate space: It does not have an inside and outside so much as it has a center and a periphery shading off into nature. You would have a hard time saying where this human realm begins and ends, who controls it, or what its most important seats are.

Figure 1.3: Mandala of the God Kalacakra, "The Wheel of Time"

One thing we can be reasonably sure of is that the campground was a place where women spent more time than men. Some anthropologists have even argued that it was the need to share child rearing and feeding that led to the establishment of the campground.[12] Whether or not this was the case, the campground was the site of two intertwined developments: the birth of architecture and matriarchy.

It seems highly probable that most Paleolithic societies were matriarchal. The women were the ones who bore children, and they were the ones who could

Figure 1.4: Alakaluf, Building a Domed Hut, Tierra del Fuego Archipelago (Chile and Argentina)

weave nature together into clothes, baskets, and tools. Women were the guardians of the future of the group, those in control of the technology that turned raw materials into food and protection, and those who probably managed to fix unspoken rules into commonly held beliefs.[13] The campground was a site of power for women and may be the place where the whole game of power got started. It began because there was a tension between this place of artifactual relations between people and things and the fears that come from the need to preserve and perpetuate oneself.

The anthropologist Claude Lévi-Strauss argued that at the heart of all society was a crime: wife snatching. To keep an early human group from disappearing through inbreeding, it was necessary to find a mate from another group. Thus a woman was removed from her site of power, her matriarchal campground, and put in the context of another group, where she was in the hands of her male captor. There she had to make a place for herself by connecting with her new sisters and relatives. She had to make a world for herself. In so doing, she also brought new customs, techniques, and forms into the household, thus invigorating and developing her new culture.[14] The dynamic that allowed early human society to evolve, but that also broke through an inclusive architecture, was rape. Rape, the most primal form of violence, is that which stands against an architecture that places, includes, and defines us.

Whether this interpretation is true or not, it certainly echoes with the countless stories of rape and the subsequent emergence of civilization that dot the myths of Greece and Mesopotamia. The whole continent of Europe derives its name from such an action. You can also argue that the very act of hunting brings an element of violence into a community or that the uncertainty of nomadic life allows both for the testing of different techniques and technology and for the need for unsettling, often violent change that comes from the profound disassociation with a given environment.

Figure 1.5: *Tent Hut and the Kraal of the Hottentots,* from Peter Kolb, *The Present State of the Cape of Good Hope . . . 1731*

There may have been many other mechanisms that controlled the population growth and development of human groups. Certainly there is an element of fear and violence that enters into the dynamic of every civilization. Why and how we again shall probably never know. I would argue that this fear leads not just to displacement but also to the creation of laws, taboos, and other forms of exclusion. Making a difference between one's self and nature becomes a paranoid act that evidences itself as a wall and as a vertical element; man standing against nature becomes an artificial construction. A place of gathering becomes a defined territory.

There are two impulses in the simple act of making a world for one's self. The first is to create a place where you can be human, can live, and can transform both yourself and nature in a never-ending process that leads from the first conscious act to the great and complicated structures of cities. The other is the impulse to exclude, to replace, and to defend. In the latter case you do not care what came before: You want only to establish yourself and your ways in the world, replacing whatever was preexisting and defending your little realm against all comers.

When we look at those people still living as nomads, or study archaeological evidence, we see two alternate ways of looking at the birth of architecture and society: as a form of weaving together the natural material present in the campground into a temporary shelter or as the creation of defense and reproductive mechanisms that create separations between people.

The nineteenth-century architect and theoretician Gottfried Semper described the beginning of architecture as follows:

> The art of dressing the body's nakedness (if we do not count the ornamental painting of one's own skin discussed above) is probably a later invention than the use of coverings for encampments and spatial enclosures. There are tribes whose savagery appears to be the most primitive who do not know clothing, yet to whom the use of skins and even a more or less developed industry of spinning, plaiting, and weaving for the furnishing and security of their encampments is not unknown. It may be that climatic influences and other circumstances are sufficient to explain this cultural-historical phenomenon, and that the normal, universally valid process of civilization cannot be absolutely deduced from it; nevertheless, it remains certain that the beginning of building coincides with the beginning of textiles. The wall is that architectural element that formally represents and makes visible the enclosed space as such, absolutely, as it were, without reference to secondary concepts. We might recognize the pen, bound together from sticks and branches, and the interwoven fence as the earliest vertical spatial enclosure that man invented, whose construction required a technique that nature, as it were, put into the hand of man. The transition from the plaiting of branches to the plaiting of basts for similar domestic purposes was easy and natural. That led to the invention of weaving, first with blades of grass or natural plant fibers, later with spun threads from vegetable or animal matter. The variations in the natural colors of the blades soon made people use them in alternating arrangements, and thus arose the pattern. Soon man surpassed these natural resources of art through the artificial preparation of materials; the dyeing and knitting of colorful carpets were invented for wall dressings, floor coverings, and canopies. Whether these inventions gradually developed in

this order or another matters little to us here, for it remains certain that the use of the crude weaving that started with the pen—as a means to make the "home," the inner life separated from the outer life, and as the formal creation of the idea of space—undoubtedly preceded the wall, even the most primitive one constructed out of stone or any other material. The structure that served to support, to secure, to carry this spatial enclosure was a requirement that had nothing directly to do with space and the division of space. It was foreign to primitive architectural thinking and was in the beginning not a form-determining element.[15]

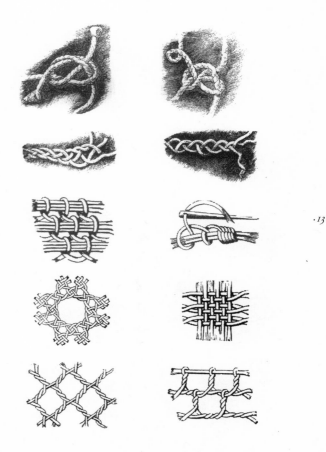

Figure 1.6: Gottfried Semper, *Knots,* 1863

The architecture of weaving precedes both the use of clothing to define and protect us and the fixed architecture of enclosure and separation. For the nomad, the tent is culture. It is the container, the expression and the total reality of his or her culture. Even when nomads such as the Aborigines of Australia do not have tents, they have a form of weaving, whether verbal or through emblematic objects, that makes sense of the world.[16] And women do the weaving.

The tent is an amazing artifact. It is constructed by combining things that grow with things that you abstract from their natural settings, like bark or woven material. You make it by combining a structural skeleton and a form of covering, though often these two are so intertwined that they are indistinguishable. It is a flexible object that you can build very easily and then change as you need; you can expand, contract, or change its direction without having to worry about foundations or even about openings. Everything can be rewoven. You might even wonder whether it is an object or a structure, as it can be either pulled apart into its constituents and carried away or can be seen as just an extension of the other artifacts of the campground, such as the firepot or the bed. [17]

The tent is the campground made into a semipermanent object. It mixes the sense of enclosure and movability that is essential to the part of human culture that divorces itself from nature and in so doing defines itself, and the round, inclusive work of building, as an actual and real culture. It is both a

Figure 1.7: Construction of Grass Structures, Southern Iraq

womb and projection, an arc that curves from the horizontal to the vertical, a place that can be dissolved, an assemblage of pieces into a flexible order. As Elizabeth Weatherford has described it:

> The dwelling the women construct usually consists of a framework woven like an inverted loose basket, covered or thatched with available materials such as large leaves, bundles of grass or woven mats. These shelters share significant characteristics across cultures. They are flexible, often

flooded with translucent light, and scented with the smoke of fires and fragrant floor coverings. They are round, ovoid or conical, with no edges or planes to interrupt the flow of space. Their size and shape maximizes physical and psychological contact among the dwellers. Anthropologists suggest that such human proximity is particularly conducive to intuitive and non-verbal communication, to the development of internalized cultural rhythms. In our Western culture, such tacit synchrony is usually found only in mother-infant relationships, a vestige of what was once the nature of communication between both sexes and all ages. A freudian [sic] theorist might suggest that the organic nature of gatherers' dwellings is a cultural extension of the biophysical environment of the womb. But in fact, these shelters can be extremely open and unwomblike. They include unsheltered areas where the work of the household, such as plaiting mats and scraping skin, takes place. The house life overflows into outdoor space, allowing the activities of its inhabitants to expand. Many gatherers' dwellings are easily adaptable, and when not easily expanded . . . there is flexibility as to who inhabits them. Children do not have to sleep with their parents, and can either stay with their grandparents or make camp with other children of the same sex at either end of the settlement. Thus the gatherers' house is not a structure enforcing family isolation, but serves as a shelter of great social fluidity. In these mobile cultures land is not individually owned and no dwelling is permanent. Women possess the building knowhow rather than the actual structures, which they may erect collectively. The building activity may be almost ritualized, as the "performer" sets into motion a body of traditional knowledge shared with other women. . . .[18]

the tent at the beginning of culture, I challenge two traditions in inking. The first is that of the "primitive hut." Popularized by the century theoretician Abbé Marc Antoine Laugier, this theory holds st architecture was not a tent but a hut, made by men as a way of utside nature.[19] To Laugier, the wall and the roof are primary, ements that replace nature completely and offer an alternative culpeculates that man first made the hut out of "defense" against the of the world. Man first went into a cave but wanted "to be housed, ," and thus created a shelter by supporting a roof on four posts.

·15·

OF PENISES AND TENTS

These posts were the prototypes for the columns that were the beginnin[g] point of all architecture. They established an order that converted nature in[to] something abstract, man-made, vertical, and orthogonal. [20]

Nowhere is woman mentioned in this story, and nowhere is there any notic[e] of society. To Laugier and his many followers, who helped define what w[e] think of as architecture (at the École des Beaux-Arts in Paris in the next ce[n]tury), architecture was an act of the willful imposition of order by a ma[n]. There is no evidence for this story, and it seems rather illogical when you thi[nk] about the much more pressing needs of food, protection, and sex. It assum[es] that our society is a clean break from nature, performed by men. The absu[r]dity of this idea is perhaps one of the reasons why architecture to this day h[as] such a tenuous place in our society: It bases itself on adding an extra, supe[r]ficial, and abstract element to the foundation myth of our society.

Yet there is a reality to this image, and that is one of monuments. W[hat] Laugier really wanted to do was base his architecture on the temples [of] the Greeks. As we shall see later on, these structures were themselves [an] expression of male, hierarchical power standing against a nature that had, [by] the time of their construction, become associated with feminized propert[ies]. The primitive hut and the whole foundation of classical architecture thus b[ase] themselves on a much later notion of how we make ourselves at home in [the] world. It was one that arose long after the original architectural acts [had] already been biased by a sexually hierarchical society.

The second myth the woven tent challenges is the primacy of an anth[ro]pocentric language. Noting that women are literally a supplement to the l[an]guage of men since their name ("wo-man") is no more than a deformati[on] colored with notions of inferiority and lack of primary value, of the w[ord] "man," feminist critics call language a "man-made prison" in which they [are] forced to dwell. [21] To Jacques Derrida, the problem is deeper than that: L[an]guage is a kind of rape of meaning from the world, an artificial construct t[hat] is necessary for the creation of rational human society but that is itself a fo[rm] of covering up or forgetting of a world known only through the senses.

Figure 1.8: Charles Eisen, "Allegory of Architecture Returning to Its Natural Model," Frontispiece to M.-A. Laugier, *L'Essai sur l'architecture*, 2nd edition, 1755

·16·

In Derrida's myth of beginnings, the first way in which we removed ourselves from the world was through language. That particular barrier, however, was still porous; it was a textual weaving, akin to the weaving of clothes or methods of storing. It allowed for a fluid community. It was the replacement of this language with writing, which removed the meaning of words from their ephemeral connection with the act of speaking, that caused a final break. As written text, language could be stored, interpreted, and thus owned. For Derrida and others, language in its broadest sense, which comprises all those cultural productions that carry meaning, including art and architecture, becomes something that not so much creates social relations out of the act of interpreting the world as it becomes, in its written and monumentalized form, the replacement of the world by an artificial one, filled with rules, regulations, and hierarchies. There is a line that runs from the removal of words from our mouths into books to the removal of all meaning from the public realm and its storage in inaccessible monuments.[22]

To these thinkers, verbal communication is a masculine invention. The development of the rules of language, the grammar that makes the world intelligible and repeatable, and the rules that derive from this process all point toward a striation of the world into layers of value. The web of written words creates a barrier in which certain people control access to meaning.

Certainly a "logocentric" society such as ours seems not only at a distance from but at war with a world of experiences. For this reason feminists have argued for other forms of art as ways of making sense of the world: dancing, magic, painting, sculpting, and weaving.[23] All these are ways in which we can understand our world by tracing it with our bodies, making it our own by placing ourselves in it, and transforming it through participation in a real, material sense. These are ways of remaking the world rather than replacing it. They are ways of dancing around the world, expressing the world rather than representing it, and spiraling away from the orders of linguistics. Against the world of language, temples, and the separation between men and women (or classes), there is, in John Dewey's words, "art as experience":

Space thus becomes something more than a void in which to roam about, dotted here and there with dangerous things and things that satisfy the appetite. It becomes a comprehensive and enclosed scene within which man engages. Time ceases to be either the endless and uniform flow or the succession of instantaneous points which some philosophers assert it to be. It, too, is the organized and organizing medium of the rhythmic ebb and flow of expectant impulse, forward and retraced movement, resistance and suspense, with fulfillment and consummations.[24]

This is an art in which it is impossible to decide what is architecture, what is useful, what is male, or what is female.

The tent was a built spiral that contained and preceded the rigid constructs of grammar and the layers of value that were the result of the creation of territory. Before there was land that was owned, and before there was an abstract language that was written down, there was the reality of the tent that made us at home in the world. It was a real place, made by men and women together. It was the scene of our humanity, one in which we made a world for ourselves. Yet the tent is also the site of the nomadic people who are removing themselves from nature and assigning a space for women and a space for men. They already defined a role for women inside and for women outside.[25]

Thus the tent and its art forms, which include dance and weaving, mimic the original tension at the dawn of human civilization: that between the desire to build a culture through the creation of a communal setting and the fear of extinction and the apprehension of an unknown world. This fear is itself replaced by the violence of displacement, whether of women or of space by building walls. The tent is the site women made and the place in which they have been ever since imprisoned:

Architecture was a domestic industry once—when every savage mother set up her own tepee. To be confined to domestic industry is no proper distinction of womanhood; it is a historic distinction, an economic distinction, it sets a date and a limit to woman's industrial progress. . . . To this same source we trace the social and educational limitations set about women. The dominant male, holding his women as property, and fiercely jealous of them, considering them always as his, not belonging to themselves, their children, or the world, has hedged them in with restrictions of a thousand sorts; physical, as in the crippled Chinese lady or the imprisoned odalisque; moral, as in the oppressive doctrines of submission taught by all our androcentric religions; mental, as in the enforced ignorance from which women are now so swiftly emerging . . . the girl-child, peering out, sees this forbidden field as belonging wholly to menkind; and her relation to it is to secure one for herself—not only that she may love, but that she may live. He will feed, clothe and adorn her—she will serve him; from the subjection of the daughter to that of the wife she steps; from one home to the other, and never enters the world at all—man's world. The boy, on the other hand, considers the home as a place of women, an inferior place, and longs to grow up and leave it—for the real world. [26]

The first cities continued the patterns of the tent, but also brought to a head that tension and played it out as a conflict between the sexes:

Two ways were in fact open for the development of human culture, once it had passed beyond the stage reached in the Neolithic community—the way of the village or the way of the citadel: or to speak in biological terms, the symbiotic and the predatory. They were not absolute choices, but they pointed in different directions. The first was the path of voluntary cooperation, mutual accommodation, wider communication and understanding: its outcome would be an organic association, of a more complex nature, on a higher level than that offered by the village community and its nearby lands. The other was that of predatory domination, leading to heartless exploitation and eventually to parasitic enfeeblement: the way of expansion, with its violence, its conflicts, its anxieties, turning the city itself into an instrument. . . .[27]

At some point in the Neolithic period, we chose the second option. This happened at the same time as, or because, we moved from a matriarchal to a patriarchal society. We also became sedentary, developed highly specialized forms of agriculture, and created places that were ruled by abstract order, whether in terms of politics, religion, or architecture. All these developments were related and led to the complete domination of women by men.

2

SPACES OF DOMINATION, TRICKS OF DOMESTICITY

WHEN WE THINK OF THE DAWN OF CIVILIZATION, we think of the great cities
of Mesopotamia. These grand citadels gave us early writing, agriculture, and
specialized social structure. Ur, Babylon, and the other permanent settle-ments
in the valley of the Euphrates and the Tigris had been great cities and were in
decline by the time of the Bible. These city-states were warlike places of
patriarchy, governed by kings who owed allegiance only to the gods and
controlled by a misogynist priest class that used women only as religious
prostitutes or handmaidens. [1]

The form of cities such as Ur represented their nature. They were fortresses,
surrounded by walls and cut through with great avenues leading to even more
enclosed palaces. In them you could find a strict hierarchy of spaces, ranging
from the undefined huts that crowded along the outer walls to the spacious
rooms of the palace that were organized around courtyards and filled with poly-
chrome decoration. The tendency of the cities was upward, to form ziggurats
that were pathways from the divine power of the skies to the orthogonal
precincts of the palace.

The form of the cities of Mesopotamia remained fairly constant from the
rebuilding of Ur in around 2230 B.C. through the rise of Khorsabad and Mari
to the metropolitan grandeur of Babylon as it appeared almost a millennium

later. Ziggurat temples and palaces were the focal points of these cities. Contained within multiple layers of walls, these precincts of the powerful focused either inward, in the case of the palaces, or upward, in the case of the religious structures. In the case of the palaces, double walls protected concentric rings, formed by double walls with storerooms in between, of spaces around a throne room and courtyard. Each precinct was more exclusive. In the case of the ziggurat, the steeply sloped sides reached up to an inner sanctum, dedicated to a male deity associated with war and the sky.

The architecture of Mesopotamia emphasized exclusion and abstraction by emphasizing how massive and tall it was. The walls of Ur, for instance, were slightly bowed to emphasize their strength. Decorations on the palace walls consisted of vertical grooves and pilaster-like lines that emphasized their vertical thrust. The interior spaces were unknown to most, exclusive, and, paradoxically, exterior. As the decorative schemes became more elaborate, they only clarified what was already implied by the architecture of these cities: They showed lines of soldiers marching toward the king, the king hunting in the forests, or the gods lording it over the earth.

Figure 2.1: Ziggurat, Ur, Third Dynasty, c. 2400 B.C.

The cities of Mesopotamia were places of power. They represented the exclusion of what was unknown, outside, and other through a mechanism of fortification and accumulation (the storerooms). They were places of walls, dark rooms, and hierarchies that tended inward and upward, leading not to a communal hearth but to an inner emptiness where no human being but only a god or king could dwell:

> In the new proto-urban milieu, the male became the leading figure; woman took second place. Her digging stick and hoe were replaced by the more efficient plow, capable, with ox-drawn power, of cleaving the heavier soils of the bottom lands. Even the female goddesses yielded in some degree to Osiris and Bacchus, precisely in the realms of agriculture and invention where woman had been most active. Woman's strength had lain in her

special wiles and spells, in the mysteries of menstruation and copulation and child birth, the arts of life. Man's strength now lay in feats of aggression and force, in showing his ability to kill and his own contempt for death: in conquering obstacles and forcing his will on other men, destroying them if they resisted. . . . This change soon left its mark over the whole landscape. Even more, it left an impress on human relations within the community. Male symbolisms and abstractions now become manifest: they show themselves in the insistent straight line, the rectangle, the firmly bounded geometric plan, the phallic tower and the obelisk, finally, in the beginnings of mathematics and astronomy, whose effective abstractions were progressively detached from the variegated matrix of myth. It is perhaps significant that while the early cities seem largely circular in form, the ruler's citadel and the sacred precinct are more usually enclosed by a rectangle.[2]

Figure 2.2: Ishtar Gate, Babylon, Iraq, c. 700 B.C.

We do not know how women lived in these cities, nor do we know how most men lived there. We do know that the creation myths of the cities talk about queens and goddesses who once ruled the society and were defeated by the kings. These goddesses' rites remained as secret cults, kept alive by small groups of women and contained within both the walls of the religious structures and the larger religious context. The myth of Ishtar or Astarte, the Queen of the Night, has become a staple of feminist history; she is the chthonic counterforce to the male Sun or War King, who rules in light, by decree, in a rational space. She is the memory of defeated nature, contained within and made invisible by the city.[3]

There were cities that were even older than Ur when the rule of women had not yet been defeated. Çatal Hüyük, in eastern Turkey, dates back to at least 6000 B.C. It is a round city, with edges that undulate back and forth along the landscape. There are no grand public spaces here, no axes cutting through the city and up into the sky. There are not even any identifiable public buildings. There is only the accumulation of private spaces, which were organized around the kitchen. There the family gathered and slept on benches, the largest of which was reserved for the wife. Religion appears to have been domestically based, and the homes were elaborately decorated with patterns derived from weaving and pottery. The overall form of the city came from the accumulation of all of these separate spaces: There were no streets, only the roofs of the houses that acted simultaneously as floors for adjacent dwellings, communal gathering spaces, and means of passage.[4]

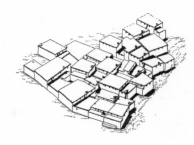

Figure 2.3: Çatal Hüyük (reconstruction), Turkey, c. 6000 B.C.

Çatal Hüyük was in many ways the campground or nomadic tent turned into a city. Roughly round, without a fixed order, decorated to resemble a tent, it had little of the grandeur of the later Mesopotamian cities. As such it does not stand alone. Knossos, for instance, the great palace city of Crete, was also an accumulation of private spaces that was designed with little regard for its exterior appearance, for overall order, or for defense. Matriarchies ruled both cities.

Yet we should be careful not to idealize such matriarchal urban environments. Though it may be true that most early settlements were matriarchal and that men wrested that power from them somewhere around 4000 B.C.,[5] that does not mean that the reign of darkness began at that point. Already a city assumes a division of labor, a way of living, and a form that do away with the flexibility of the nomad settlement.

Figure 2.4: Plan, Çatal Hüyük, Turkey, c. 6000 B.C.

I would go even further. If we can imagine the nomads as bands of loosely organized human beings roaming a nature that stretches out all around them, without clear limits and with boundless possibilities, the first act of removal in which they engage is the marking of a fixed and permanent territory. The discovery of agriculture brings with it ownership, a fact that we can see and understand not just as an abstract concept but as a line drawn in the sand, a fence, a wall, a gridded row of furrows that runs in a different direction from those on the plot next to it. With agriculture and settlements starts the process that the French thinker Gilles Deleuze has called striation.[6] If the nomad inhabited "smooth" space and wove textiles that were continuous, flowing, expansive, inclusive, and without a fixed meaning, then the settler occupies a "striated" or stratified space. In that space nature disappears underneath the markers of territory, and the markers of territory lose their relative value as laws and regulations begin to govern their appearance. Similarly, real goods derived from the land begin to lose their value in favor of the shape or transformation wrought on them by human labor. That value is, as Marx pointed out long ago, removed from its source and stockpiled, creating the flexible flows of capital that stand in for the original flow of the nomadic landscape.[7]

Friedrich Engels, Marx's partner, was the first to point out that the emergence of this stratified space coincided with the submission of women to men.[8] Feminists argue about the timing and reason for this.[9] Some maintain that men, as the hunters who provided the food for the nurturing mothers, were more adept at using tools and thus soon controlled technology that split apart the smooth surfaces of the earth to replace it with a man-made landscape.[10] Others have pointed out that it was women who controlled technology in the tent or around the campground and speculate that it was the violent, paranoid nature of the male hunting party that wrenched control of these tools from women.[11] A whole countermyth has grown up in recent years. In this story women once ruled a peaceable world in which all were at one with nature. Men, chafing under the yoke of the matriarchy, revolted and wrested power from the women. Ever since then men, fearful of a power that predates theirs and realizing that their world is an artificial one that is not really of their making, have kept women locked up.[12]

I do not know how much truth there is to this story. Certainly the disappearance of the world of the nomad, the emergence of fixed settlements and the technology of agriculture all led to the emergence of an economic, social, and religious system governed by strict rules, hierarchies, and men. If you imagine the world of the state, you see a world of straight streets and walls, palaces, lines, and monuments. These contain and embody an artificial division between sexes as well as classes (and often races) that is played out in narratives and rituals, including in our own Bible, in which the rule of patriarchy, the setting of rigid laws descending from the skies, and the importance of abstract value systems completely bury the reality of the world.[13]

This world is at least partially founded on the submission of women. Women did the real work of child rearing, cooking, and maintaining the home, while men engaged in the artificial work of war, trading, and ruling—at least ideally. In reality, of course, this held true only for the ruling classes. That ideal was embedded in one central aspect of the early city: the notion of public space. The king and the aristocracy needed a space all their own where they could appear, a space that was not part of nature and not productive, but just a place of power. It was a world conquered and emptied out by force. A man who could gain enough power or prestige would want to enter this world of emptiness. There he could define himself as something other than his body. He could partake of a world of appearances, of hierarchically arranged forms and meanings. This was the public space, the place of appearance, the place that gave meaning to the act of defense that created the walled-in city, the place where stories were told and fixed in murals, where rites were enacted, where men were made.[14]

This was a different space from the woven world of women. They remained inside, around the hearth, surrounded by their stories. They became, to a large extent, invisible. Of course, this story of separation is a simplification. Only in the Middle East, in the time between the founding of Ur and the emergence of the biblical patriarchy, does it appear to have worked so blatantly. In many societies today you can still see communal structures that are not segregated by sex, where the hearth survives as a religious focus, though riven apart by certain hierarchies and lines. Think, for instance, of the pueblo at Taos, an accumulation of private dwellings, organized around sunken round *kivas* and separated into clans by the river that comes down from the Sangre de Cristo Mountains. Here the relationship between men and women and between defined space and nature is much more fluid and complex than in Middle Eastern societies.[15]

Our society, fortunately or unfortunately, is based on the traditions that emerged out of Mesopotamia and Egypt. The latter country became—despite the rule of a few queens—the place that crystallized male power into the pyramids, temples, and avenues of pharaonic power. The pyramids are themselves the ultimate expression of power; useless monuments for dead males, they represent the accumulation of a tremendous amount of labor and capital that is just buried and made useless.[16] They are governed by a completely abstract

Figures 2.5: Pyramid of Chefren and Sphinx, Giza, c. 2500 B.C.

and inhuman scale and geometry; they cannot be entered or even comfortably climbed and have no direct relationship to any aspect of the surrounding landscape. Instead they relate to the heavens, to a mental picture of perfection, and to a notion of the ascent of man into another, nonhuman realm.

There have been many theories about the pyramids, but the most salient point about them is their shape. They are giant abstractions from the reality of everyday life and daily experiences. They convert the horizontal labyrinth of a striated world through which we all move into an ordered, enclosed, inflexible, unusable thrust upward to a realm that we cannot enter unless we become something else than human—namely, dead. They stand in splendid isolation as the perfect emblem of that bane of male-dominated society—namely, the monument. More than the ziggurats, pyramids represent the tendency of power to enshrine and fix itself in an object that defies and defines human lives. More than the play of power, they are the tomb of power itself.

Of course, there was more to Egypt than the pyramids. There was the sphinx, the half-female, half-animal guardian that perhaps stood as a reminder of feminine power, here also entombed in an inflexible and mysterious object. The sphinx has continued to operate throughout Western civilization as the image of what we have made women: mysterious, unknowable, questioning, and causing our very existence. It is something so ancient and so unknowable that it questions our rational pursuit of meaning and power.[17]

Figure 2.6: Aerial View, Rural Midwest

Camille Paglia has called the Nile itself the "first straight line in western culture," cut through the desert as "a phallic track of mind piercing the entanglements of nature" that converge in the pyramids. "In Egypt, construction is male geometry, a glorification of the visible."[18] Certainly she is right that the agricultural empire of Egypt fixed male domination in abstract geometric forms. Since the days of the pyramids and Sumerian palaces, there have been two forms that represent the replacement of nature with a man-made world: the grid and the tower. The grid is originally the furrowed field, later further defined with walls or fences and repeated in the patterns of city streets until it becomes the abstract ideal for both building and urban planning. The vertical point is the storage of the value derived from the earth, whether directly as silos or bins holding wheat or as the abstracted accumulation of wealth and power in the case of palaces and temples.

The architectural historian Vincent Scully used to show a slide comparing grain silos in the American Midwest with the Cathedral of Chartres rising out

of the rolling wheat fields.[19] Though the comparison might seem absurd when you think about the very different functions and forms of these two structures, it makes sense: Both represent, in their vertical thrust, the condensation and conversion of the plains into an abstract form. It is a form that we associate with male power, precisely because it both has phallic connotations and is the very real result of a male-dominated, aggressive, and power-based attitude toward the way we live in and experience the real world. The vertical form has little to do with living, with gathering, or even with understanding the world. Instead it stands in the world as an abstract shape that is either essentially a tool (of storage) or a symbol of the power that gained from, but is separate from, the world through that tool. That power can be religious, secular, or, as is the case in the skyscrapers of today, economic.

Figure 2.7: Torre Asinelli, Torre Garisenda, Bologna, Italy, 1109–10

The grid, meanwhile, is a trickier form. It contains and constrains the forms of everyday life. In Egypt, as in the later architecture of Mesopotamia like the palace of Persepolis, it becomes a sea of columns, each a miniature of the male form standing against the sky, holding up the orthogonal beams that keep the real world out and create an artificial, interior world. Architectural historians have long debated the proliferation of columns in the so-called hypostyle halls like the one in Karnak (circa 1290 B.C.), yet I would argue that whatever its technical or religious merits, the sea of columns does nothing so much as convert the abstract power of the grid, with its controlling and defining overtones, into a very real, intimidating, and all-encompassing reality in which most men and all women have no real place. Wandering through the hypostyle hall, you are lost in a sea of order.

The hall at Karnak stood, like most Egyptian temple precincts, at the end of long pathways, axes that were the other legacy of Egypt's early architecture. The axis is a way of swerving from the ordinary into the predetermined. Along the axis your expectations are met because ideally everything you encounter has been designed in a sequence. At its most simple, an axis provides you with a sequence of light and dark, tall and low, open and closed. It becomes ever tighter and often higher, until you reach a culmination point at which you transfer into another world (the pyramid) or, later, merely into another state (the triumphal arch that marked the entrance to the precincts of Roman power). The axis is the narrative made real. Remember that the narrative is part of the patriarchal way of subsuming reality into a rational system that is both word- and sight-based. Instead of the spiraling cycles of tales told around the hearth and still preserved in the early metamorphic traditions of antiquity, in which the only end of a tale was the transformation of the hero into something else, before he or she then became something else again, like Leda becoming a constellation, the narrative or axial progression takes an unformed person and transforms him (rarely her) into a perfectly sculpted personality that stands in sharp contrast with his surroundings. Usually he achieves this result by the acquisition of an object such as the grail. These narratives are all about defining yourself as something separate from and beyond the world, often by taking a symbolic piece out of it. They are about grabbing power, abstracting it, and moving along a line that goes away from the real world, away from community, and away from the womb from which you were born.

Figures 2.8: Cathedral, Chartres, 1194–1230

·29·

Figure 2.9: Hypostyle Hall, Temple of Amon-ra, Karnak, c. 1290 B.C.

Figure 2.10: Avenue of the Ram-Headed Sphinxes, Thebes, c. 1400 B.C.

Whatever the particular nature or meaning of the journey, the axis itself is a rather unworldly and deadly space. It is laid out with little regard for topography except in an abstract sense, as when it is aligned with certain mountaintops, river crossings, or celestial patterns. It cuts through the complications of daily life and leads to only one place. It is a projection, a phallic extension. It is also, of course, a very useful and rational tool for navigating your way through space. Going in a straight line toward an identifiable object makes life a lot simpler. Yet in that very simplicity the contradictions and layering of everyday life are somehow often lost.

Thus by the time of the pharaohs the essential lines of Western architecture were set. They were the monumental, vertical objects of storage, transcendence, and abstraction; the grid of control; the axis that tied together and made sense out of the grid and the object. I would not argue that the emergence of this way of defining a man-made reality was a conspiracy, nor was it a conscious attempt to replace nature and the power of women. The reality of the socioeconomic development of Western society merely evidences itself in these forms, so that the oppressive, totalitarian culture of accumulation and aggression takes on these forms: "Beginning as the concentration of manpower under a firm, unified, self-reliant leadership, the ancestral city was primarily an instrument for regimenting man and mastering nature, directing the community itself to the service of gods."[20]

As soon as these forms emerge, they become a reality that we all have to live in. They define in turn the logic of the development of society. They create the boundaries, the centers, and the entrances of places of power. Those included in the precincts of wealth and power will seek to perpetuate their world, while those on the outside will either want in or want to destroy these artificial precincts. Thus the actual spatial reality of culture becomes the catalyst of social action. The sieges of foreigners and the revolutions of the have-nots, often leading to their encampment in the precincts of power for a period of time just long enough to cause somebody to want to replace them, are spatial events. The plays of power, the desire of men, and the ownership of the means of production are made real in the fortresses of accumulation.

The one conflict that is completely submerged in these forms is that between men and women. The game of conquest is one played by men. Women are buried underneath the great forms of the pyramids and replaced by the grids of columns. They retreat inside, into space where they are often not seen or heard. They become the invisible foundation of the fanciful creations of men. Women do not try to usurp the tower, the grid, and the axis. They do not engage in these overt games of power. Instead they subvert them.

It is interesting to note that the largest complex in Egypt associated with a woman, the palace of Queen Hatshepsut (circa 1480 B.C.), is partially buried in a cliff. Though fronted with a full panoply of columns and reached by an axis that is not only grand but also vertical, it glorifies the condition women found themselves in: buried and out of sight. The space of women was already the space of the home, where they could gather in small groups in courtyards or in the streets when they were engaged in the activities of daily life, such as washing or getting water. They left no permanent traces and controlled no space. Their forms were the ephemeral and useful arts of weaving and basketry, so that their representations disappeared in use and time. That does not mean that their lives or their spaces were any the less real. It just means that few traces remain. Women in the age of patriarchy were removed from that part of space that aspires to permanence, just as they were removed from the annals of history that were written as the progression of great and meaningful deeds by men.

There is something ephemeral about the space of women. The courtyard is not a place that has its own contours but is usually defined by the buildings around it. Similarly, the streets in the cities that women actually used, as opposed to the ceremonial axes, were defined by function more than by abstract principles. The space of women was not a place of appearance, of representation, of

Figure 2.11: *Boulevard Richard Lenoir, Paris, from Alphand's* Promenades de Paris, *1867–1873*

fixed principles. It was a flexible accumulation of areas that responded to the needs for shelter, child rearing, eating, and sleeping. It could change according to the needs of its inhabitants and could be rebuilt as it was necessary. For many centuries the basic building blocks of the city remained the same all through the Mediterranean and Middle East: simple mud or mud-brick enclosures that together formed a finely grained pattern of inhabitation. It was a place of smooth surfaces, often rounded at its edges, and of a lack of strong contrasts in either colors or the height of buildings. It is the background, the context, the texture and textile of the city that still survives today.

Figure 2.12: Albert Speer,
Proposal for Berlin, c. 1936

Women were thus deprived of their ability to enter into the plays of power because they could usually not gain access to, build, or define those forms that would identify them as something more than just a human being and instead invest them with rank, privilege, wealth, and a particular identity. Women were no place and thus were no one, at least in the grand scheme of things. Inside their no-places, however, they still lived and made a world for themselves. It was a world men often feared and thus tried to contain. The idea of the harem, purdah, or women's space dates back to biblical times, when the woman had to be contained and kept out of sight. She was part of the background, part of what the man owned; she was real estate in the strictest and most elemental sense.

In many ways the woman became embedded in the city. It is probably no coincidence that we often personify cities as women, which are seen as realms of femininity as opposed to the masculinity of nature. In fact, one of the recurring themes in Western history, from the Song of Songs to the stories of the

Moors in Spain, is that of the rulers who conquer or build a city only to become feminized by living in it. Instead of narratives that are axial, the elliptical spaces of love songs appear, set in places defined by layers of curtains and veils. The veil becomes the mask where the woman can appear: as a shadow or impression that has only a temporary presence in space, something that one moves through or past or something that hides and transforms the reality of enclosure, while the man appears out in the open: "She maketh herself coverings of tapestry; her clothing is silk and purple. Her husband is known in the gates, when he sitteth among the elders of the land."[21]

We can speculate about the spaces of the ruling classes of early Mediterranean civilizations as developed interiors. They were most likely nebulous realms that opened onto the courtyard but were also open to visitors. Though they might have walls, they more often than not were defined by curtains or merely by the presence of light and fire. They were thus formalized versions of the campground, turned into sophisticated, gauzy, and ephemeral spaces that women defined and often made within the precincts established by men. What dominated these spaces were probably objects, the furnishings that were transforming the poses of everyday life into stances. Chairs, sofas, beds, and chests formalized the functions of lying, standing, sitting, and storing into a quasi-architectural position. Furniture appeared as the halfway point between architecture and the body.[22]

Figure 2.13: Throne Room of the Megaron, Palace of Nestor, Pylos, c. 1200 B.C.

It is easy to become romantic about such spaces. We know them from the Hollywood epics as places of light music, sex, intrigue, and luxury. Whether or not they were as lavish and beautiful as we now imagine, we shall never really know since only a few fragments of them remain. It does appear, however, that if there was any place where life could be lived by both men and women in a state that reached beyond either the needs of everyday life or the plays of power, it was in the gauzy room off the courtyard, the contained space of the harem, the nascent interior.

Perhaps this is why some historians have described the palace of Knossos as nothing but a sequence of interiors. Lavishly decorated, labyrinthine, and often not enclosed, the palaces of Crete stand in contrast with the fortresses to the

·34·

east and south of this island. Perhaps this was because the wealth of Crete came from trade rather than conquest or agriculture. This was a society based on the exchange of goods, rather than on capture and control. It was also probably a matriarchy.[23]

Vincent Scully has pointed out that there was a direct relationship between the elaborate interiors of Knossos and the surrounding mountains.[24] These were not spaces that separated themselves off from the world but rather were spaces where the world was converted or transformed into something on the level of an object one could hold, a space that had certain contours, and an art of wall coverings that itself conventionalized nature into waves, figures, and beasts that were half real, half monumental.

Figure 2.14: View from the Palace of Knossos to Mount Ida

The qualities of the palace of Knossos present an alternative to both the undefined shapes of Çatal Hüyük and the concentric hierarchies of Mesopotamia and Egypt. They are places where geometries do not lead to one point, but rather lead around in spiraling motions between courtyards, moving both up and down with the landscape. The walls are massive but also open up the world around. Of course, these were rarefied precincts in which probably only the select few lived, and for all we know, the spaces in which the lower classes lived were as hierarchical or as anonymous as those of any other Mediterranean city. Yet Knossos itself shows how male and female, open and closed, up and down can be woven together into a labyrinth of richly varied and connected spaces.

How different are the spaces of mainland Greece to which we look today as the models for our architecture. They are spaces that separate themselves off from nature and replace it with an alien presence. The history of Greek architecture, from the pre-Mycenaean fortresses and temples dedicated to goddesses to the apotheosis of classic form on the Acropolis in Athens, shows the emergence of ever-straighter, more isolated, and more masculine forms: "The old landscape of the goddess is infused with human mind, and the symmetry of a classic Zeus falls over the land and sea, exactly as, at Olympia, his dominion had led the Greeks, almost without willing it, to shape space itself as a living and palpable thing."[5]

It is easy to trace this development in ceremonial structures. Whereas archaic Greek buildings were embedded both in the landscape and in the fabric of everyday life, often amounting to no more than some spaces or aspects of a palace dedicated to a divinity, the palaces of Mycenae are isolated fortresses reserved for rulers. When the temples of Hera, the goddess who becomes nothing more than the wife of Zeus, started to appear in seventh century B.C., they were isolated objects. Based on the *megaron*, or inner courtyard, which was nothing more than a formalization of forms around the campfire or hearth, the sacred area becomes embedded in ever more complicated and sophisticated architectural forms. First it turns from an outdoor to an indoor space, deprived of sunlight and a visual relationship to the surrounding landscape. Then it becomes an isolated object whose peaked roof and enclosing walls assert its independence.

Figure 2.15: Temple of Apollo, Corinth, c. 600 B.C.

By the time the temples of Apollo, Zeus, and Poseidon start to appear in the sixth and fifth centuries B.C., the temple has become a compact, carefully balanced composition. Rectangular, set on a plinth, surmounted by a peaked roof, and either surrounded or fronted by one row of columns, it is an object unlike a house, a funerary mound, or a palace. It is a place for beings that look like humans, but only in a removed way: the Olympian gods. The temple is a place that presents another world, a world of magic and great deeds that is controlled by those who tell its tales and perform its rites. Though there are goddesses and priestesses, more and more that power is held by men, and more and more the temple becomes a defined type. It often stands on a rocky promontory, as if in defiance of nature. The number and

Figure 2.16: Parthenon, Athens,
c. 447–438 B.C.

Figure 2.17: Phidias, *Statue of Athena*
(reconstruction), Parthenon, Athens,
c. 447–438 B.C.

height of its various elements become carefully calibrated, designed according to complicated laws that only certain men know. What goes on inside, the mysterious rites where nature and women might still have a force, is carefully hidden and isolated. Instead of this mystery, the temple stands clearly alone in the light.

By the time you reach the top of the Acropolis in Athens, you have removed yourself from the city proper. You have passed through the propylaea, or gates. Your relationship to the surrounding countryside has been rearranged. Though the central temple is dedicated to a goddess, it is a desexed figure.[26] Its columns are so refined that they have no resemblance to the wood or stone out of which they must originally have been made and are instead just abstract vertical lines. Grooved and molded, they stand as repetitive elements in an order of building and theology that is removed from everyday life. They support a complicated linear system of interlocking structural and ornamental pieces, including metopes and friezes, which combine both to cover the building with a kind of writing, a picture book of the deeds of gods or the polis, or city, and to serve to create a spatial order that stands in defiance of gravity, rather than in recognition of it. These are not tents or even the regularized and geometricized earth mounds of Egypt and Mesopotamia. These are abstractions: "In the light everything is simple and grave. The relation of the buildings to each other and to the land fuses in the white light. What remains is beyond action, too instantaneous for reverie, too deep for calm. It is silence, the sweet deep breath taken. Time stops. Fear lies dead upon the rock. The column is. It stands."[27]

This is the main fact about Greek religious architecture. It stands, outside nature, outside human gathering, as an isolated monument to man's achievement. It is a dead and forbidding place, a place of importance that makes an artificial order of language, laws, and economic logic real. The Parthenon embodies the supreme achievement of Greek civilization: to create a complete man-made world.

This world is made real not just on the Acropolis but in all spaces of public gathering and in all Greek colonies. The agora, or public market place, is not just a central gathering point but a place marked by lines of columns that create a shaded colonnade around a void: "The entire public area of Athens consisted of an alternation of enclosed inner spaces and colonnaded semi-open areas. Curiously, the design of private dwellings featured the exact inverted pattern: in the standard plan a number of rooms were arranged around an inner courtyard, with only one outlet to the street."[28] The place where men gather, make decisions, play, and seduce each other is a void defined by an abstract, repetitive order.

Figure 2.18: Agora Viewed Through Reconstructed Stoa, Priene, 2nd century B.C.

Public space has become a symbol of everything that architects and planners think is important in the cities we build today. They equate public open space with a sense of community, a sense of power, and a sense of freedom. Yet the space of the agora is merely an empty place where politics or commerce play itself out. It is not a great space, just a place where certain things are lacking, space that has not been filled by man and woman. It is a place that makes into a defined, inhabitable space the fact that all the important social and economic structures we create are founded on abstract ideas and are a remove from direct experience. It is also a place that reminds us that this space of intellectual freedom is created through the erection of walls that keep out.

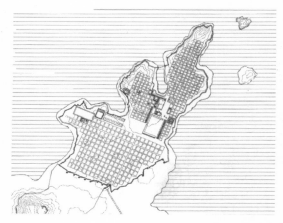

Figure 2.19: City Plan, Miletus, (Turkey), after 479 B.C.

In the few centuries that the Greek city-states achieved mastery over most of the eastern Mediterranean, they colonized countless islands and seaside areas with their abstract—in both a physical and a socioeconomic sense—forms. Colonies like Miletus were grids, laid out over the natural contours and organized around large, empty public spaces. They were cities of hierarchy, not just between the colonizers and the native inhabitants, or among the inhabitants, or among the men and women of the inhabitants, but between

SPACES OF DOMINATION, TRICKS OF DOMESTICITY

nature and the man-made, the old and the new, the inside and the outside, the significant spaces and buildings and the homes that filled in the gridded squares with the anonymous forms in which everyday life was lived.

Women were not just kept out of the agora but were kept at home. As much as the Greek city and its buildings were defined by appearance, so the home and women were defined by a lack of appearance, a resolute interiority. In the Greek polis you *were* only when you appeared as someone or something. Men went around naked quite often, and public speaking and performance were the centers around which power turned:

> For the "respectable" classes of Attic society, the anatomical differences between men and women were translated into the shapes of their living spaces: women's reproductive organs are internal and, to the ancients, were mysterious; their outer shape camouflages rather than accentuates them. Men's genitals on the other hand are conspicuous, and expressive of desire and aggression. Analogously, women spent their lives wrapped in veils, nameless, concealing their identity and locked away in the dark recesses of closed-in homes. Men spent their lives in open areas, in the sunlit spaces of the Agora and other public domains, which were off limits to women except on special occasions. There men displayed their skills and their genitals and indulged their thirst for identity and immortality through fame.[29]

Women were not to be seen. They went covered and were confined at home as much as possible. When they did appear, they were either whores or oddities. The misogyny of Greek culture was severe. Philosophers supported wife beating and argued that women were not quite human.[30] This attitude was formalized in the house. From what we can gather, both from archaeological evidence and by observing modern Greek dwellings, the house was an anonymous, rather flexible affair. Its public spaces were at the front and were reserved for men. Women lived in dark, often unlit spaces. The only place where man and woman came together was on the narrow *klimen,* or marriage bed, and then only for purposes of reproduction. On vases women are shown weaving or engaged in other crafts. They are often associated with furniture.[31]

The pattern for the development of European domestic architecture was set: grand and carefully defined spaces of appearance for men; anonymous, dark, and craft-oriented interior realms for women. Whether these spaces were the result or a symptom of a relationship of power caused by economic forces or they in fact embodied and fixed otherwise fluid social relations, Greek philosophy built a complicated architecture of exclusion and difference on the simple split between inside and outside, public and private, appearance and hidden, man and woman:

> For as *gaster* ["a thrust to the belly," or embodiment of the fact that woman feeds and makes defenseless the man] the woman literally embodies the principle of corporeality, the fact of mortality; as *gaster* she represents everything associated with interiority—hollowness, deceit, death. If men cannot escape her, they can construct a realm which excludes her—the realm of the *agora*, world of pure *logos*, at once both fictional and real. If she is a fiction, an artifice, she is also the principle of reality, the reality of the *gaster*. Although men cannot escape this reality, they can construct a fiction to counter it—the fiction of a world without women.[32]

Figure 2.20: Athenian Houses (reconstruction), 5th–4th Century B.C.

Thus the Greeks constructed the principles of the physical world we inhabit to this day. That world is one governed by *Logos,* or pure thought, and realized as empty spaces surrounded by an abstract architecture. This is a world whose main function is to exclude the real world and women. Those two are identified as the same. At the same time, woman is identified as an artifice, as something or someone that is subverting and threatening to destroy the carefully constructed male orders, because at home she is creating another realm, one both within the realm of male control and beyond his comprehension. There she is an object of desire and a mechanism of reproduction, thus robbing man of the sense of autonomy or difference out of which he has erected his self-image. The grand orders of male architecture divide the sexes—as well as the classes, since only the full-blooded Athenians or members of any particular city-state were allowed to be part of the public ritual—while encasing within themselves their own critique.

Thus architecture is an ambivalent activity. When we construe it as the making of significant buildings and spaces, it is the activity of men. Yet there is another architecture, the architecture of weaving and tricking, the architecture of deceit, conceit, and trickery. This is the architecture of women. It is an architecture that is closely associated with technology or the ability to remake the world in order for it to serve human needs and ends. The critic Ann Bergren traces the roots of this architecture back to the notion of a *metis,* or trick:

Figure 2.21: *Women Weaving,* Attic Black-Figure Vase, c. 550 B.C.

> *Metis* embraces both mental and manual prowess, both language and material. *Metis* works by continual shape-shifting, turning the *morphe* [form] of defeat into victory's tool. Its methods include the trick or trap (*dolos*), the profit-gaining scheme (*kerdos*), and the ability to seize the opportunity (*kairos*). Each of these exploits the essential form of metis, the "turning" (*tropos*) that binds opposites, manifest in the reversal and the circle, in weaving, twisting, and knotting, and in every joint. The mistress or master of *metis* knows how to manipulate "the circular reciprocity between what is bound and what is binding." Etymologically, *metis* is derived from the verbal root meaning "to measure," with its implication of calculation and exact knowledge. A traditional connection between *metis* and the builder's skills is seen in the figure of Athena, daughter of the goddess Metis, who teaches the making (*poiesai*) of elaborate war chariots to "builder men" (*tektonas andras*) and weaving to maidens (*parthenikas*), and in the mythological architect Trophonius. The Greek myth of *metis* dramatizes the mutual construction of architecture, gender, and philosophy under the sign of "father-ruled" marriage.[33]

Such an architecture is one that translates the real world into a manufactured one, not by imposing an abstract structure like a grid, an axis, or a geometry on it but by using the properties and contours of materials in new combinations. It is a technology that continually pushes material to the breaking point and tests the possibilities. It is an experimental architecture that weaves new structures out of what is already known.[34] It is the manner in which the tradition of the hearth and tent is translated into the forms of the city and remains embedded within the alien and harsh forms of a male architecture.

The woman, sitting at home, develops her crafts into a kind of countermech-
anism. To the Greeks, this division goes back to the tales of Homer. While
Odysseus roams the seas and does his great deeds out in space, Penelope sits
at home and weaves the tales together, reconstructing her world every day and
pulling it apart at night. She is the victim of a male regime in which she is an
object that stands not for herself but for the male's power and wealth. Yet as
several critics have pointed out, this makes her a sign, something that has no
direct connection to reality but only stands for something. A sign, they point
out, is dangerously free because it belongs to whoever can manipulate it to
mean what he or she wants. As a sign for male power, as a beautiful object
that is the man's most prized possession, or as that which stands for the
wealth to be gained through rape and capture, the woman is not so much real
as a floating image that moves through the reality of everyday life. As that
which is added to the male world, that which comes after the male, that which
allows the male to reproduce himself, she is an additional factor, something
that is an add-on and thus not caught by the bounds of necessity. From the
time of the Greeks onward women are associated with ornament, that which
is added on to a logically constructed building not in order to make it stand
up or function better but either to adorn it or to make it communicate some
aspect of power and beauty.[35] As such, ornament is something that you can
remove without damaging the fundamental integrity or power of the building
yet that is essential for it to be an embodiment of social relations by
communicating the purpose and values of the building. All this makes the
woman dangerous:

> A woman must be movable so that men can communicate. She must
> enclose so that he can support. But if the female can move, her placement
> is uncertain. If she can weave, she can also unweave space and place.
> What makes marriage possible, makes its stability uncertain. So this con-
> straint of the female architectural capacity is both health and harm, requir-
> ing its own architectural antidote, the immovable (re)marriage bed.[36]

Thus, says Bergren, we can rethink architecture not as great temples and great
deeds performed by men for men but as a tricky subversion or elision of the
structures we inhabit:

Mêtis means the power and the product of "transformative intelligence"—
the mental and material process common to every *techne*, to the work of
every artisan. It embraces both mind and hand, both language and material. *Mêtis* thus integrates powers and activities separated in aesthetic traditions that draw a sharp line between the verbal and the visual, between
the linguistic and the plastic, the written text and the building. It means
continual shape-shifting, imitating the form of your enemy and defeating
him with your trick at his own game. . . . It is the reversal and the circle,
each as the polymorphous double of the other. It is thus weaving and
twisting and knotting. It is every joint.[37]

The architecture of the woman is built into the very joinery and reality of the
abstract orders of male space. It cannot be denied.

Bergren goes on to argue that there is a model for a space which is that of
women outside of, beyond, and before the space of men. The space of the
feminine for Bergren is the *chora,* or space that precedes framed, defined, and
active space in Greek thought. The *chora* is the emptiness that is filled by
creation, the space that cannot be properly named, known, or defined. It is
neither masculine nor feminine but offers a way out of that dichotomy: "But
an active *chorâ*— an active, non-metaphysical, material event— . . . would be
the work of architecture outside of participation in the Forms, architecture
outside of transcendental metaphysics—before the feminization of practical
building in compensation for philosophical construction. It would be pre-
architectural architecture, a building before building."[38] This may be too vague
and abstract a space ever to imagine inhabiting. It is, however, an emptiness
that is filled with possibilities and is located in the very foundation of Western architecture, thought, and social relations, threatening to destabilize all of
its carefully created columns of power.

Figure 2.22: Pintoricchio, *The Homecoming of Ulysses* from *Scenes from the Odyssey*, c. 1513

3

CROSSROADS AND CRYPTS

THE FIRST THING THE ROMANS DID when they set up camp in one of the many territories they had conquered was to set up a cross—not a vertical cross but one that they embedded in the landscape itself. It was made by the *cardo* and the *decumanus,* the two principal streets that divided the Roman encampment, or *castrum*, into four parts. The first of these usually ran north-south and originally connected the camp to Rome. The *decumanus* intersected this line of expansion, making a place out of a line of conquest. These two orthogonal lines connected the outpost to Rome while laying out an alien, reproducible system of order on Hungarian steppes, English fields, French hills, and African sands. From Scotland to Algeria, you can still find these two streets at the heart of cities. They are the prototype for our main street, for the crossing point where commerce begins and from which power emanates.

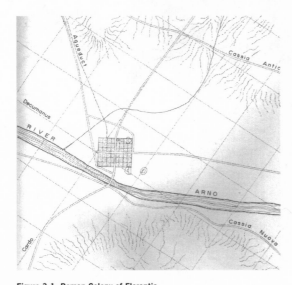

Figure 3.1: Roman Colony of Florentia
(later Florence, Italy), c. 59 B.C.

The crossing of the *cardo* and the *decumanus* is fundamentally different from the gathering point of the campfire. The campfire is a generator, a cause of technological transformation, a gathering point around which people can weave a culture. It becomes the tent, the home, and all other spaces where people come together to make the world their own. The crossroads is not a place. In most Roman camps, it was enlarged to become a square. It is a void that facilitates order. It is a place you move through, on foot, on horseback, or later in a car. Buildings surround this active empty place and derive their order from it: They face the main street; they line it; they become more private as the spaces move back from the noise of the street. The crossroads is a kind of embodiment of the *chora,* or empty space, but in a perverse way. It cannot be inhabited, nor is it a place of nature. It is, however, a place of flows and of ceaseless energy. It is a place where you dissolve into movement.[1]

Figure 3.2: Reconstruction, Roman Camp at Gloucester, c. 100

All that movement remains constricted by the rigid geometry of the two crossing roads. The road represents power: the power to control the landscape and all it produces; the power to assert a foreign order on the landscape; the power to create a new world on top of the old one. It is a power that cites: It cites Rome; it cites abstract rules of geometry; it cites the laws and regulations that are written down in books.[2] It also sites, creating the site of such power and siting the buildings that make that power real. In so doing, it ignores what is real, what is already there, and what has its own forms.

The Roman crossing is at the heart of a system of urban and architectural planning that completes the orders of abstraction marked by male domination. It was a brutal order, but also one that started much of what we know as Western civilization on its way to law and order. The Roman encampment became a city, the fields that surrounded it mimicked the geometry of the crossroads, and the roads themselves connected every place to a center of civilization where culture was constructed. Roman culture outside Rome became real first as a set of lines in the ground, then as an elaboration of those lines in walls, buildings, and open spaces where commerce took place. That world centered on public spaces and buildings from which women and natives were excluded or within which they were contained. These temples, marketplaces, and villas were the physical embodiment of Roman rule and the catalyst for the development of cities, forms, and structures of order all around them.

The rules that governed this order were codified in the first century B.C. by the architectural theoretician Vitruvius, whose *The Ten Books of Architecture* became the bible for all future architects.[3] According to Vitruvius, the architect is someone who translates a large amount of abstract knowledge about history, the physical world, and philosophy into a fixed form. He does this by fitting this knowledge into forms that he arranges according to an order, or *taxis* (the Greek word from which "taxonomy" derives). This order is one of arrangement, or putting things in their proper places, in a way that is strictly hierarchical or "proportional." The rules of this hierarchy have to do with the proper way in which one sites and cites the human body, which is the standard of measurement of all proportions, and how one then translates that body into larger, more abstract relationships that evoke a nebulous quality known as beauty.[4] It is not any human body, however, but the male body whose ideal measurements Vitruvius subjects to a rigid taxonomy. He makes it clear that we are talking about not a real body but an ideal, statuesque male form that has only a tangential relationship to the complexities of the actual human body.[5]

The work of architecture begins, however, not with the making of a building but with the siting of a city in an empty terrain in such a manner that it is both healthful and easily defensible.[6] That site must first be defined by walls.[7] Thus Vitruvius bases the very act of founding a new city on fear and exclusion of nature and the unknown. The order of the city, which follows the order of the crossroads, elaborates itself according to the cardinal directions and the position of the stars, so that a grand cosmic order is translated into the world of inhabitable order.

It is not until Vitruvius has told us what an architect needs to know, what the abstract principles of architecture are, and how we need to begin by clearing out a space for the making of buildings that is outside nature that he steps back and tells us how architecture started and of what it is made. "Some persons, however, may find fault with the position of this book, thinking that it should have been placed first," he concedes. However, "Being engaged in writing a complete treatise on architecture, I resolved to set forth in the first book the branches of learning and studies of which it consists, to define its departments, and to show of what it is composed. . . . This book is, therefore, in its proper order and place."[8] Only once he has constructed an ideal man and an ideal place that are separate from the world has he created order, both in the world and in his text. Rather than trace the complexities of everyday life, he is constructing another world.

Figure 3.3: Sanctuary of Asklepios (reconstruction), Kos, Greece, c. 300–150 B.C.

·47·

In this manner Vitruvius defines the hierarchy of architecture that puts ideas about proportion, arrangement, and order first, the idea of defense second, and then subordinates the reality of the building, its building material and the way it has developed from the logic of its construction. It is worth pointing out that in his history of architecture Vitruvius speculates that the first dwellings were formalizations of the campground and that they were woven together out of the branches of trees rather than autonomous objects. Yet that history, along with the reality of building material, is completely suppressed by the later "perfection" of architecture that derives its essential forms from the temple, which is the first actual building form Vitruvius discusses once he has laid down his fundamental principles.

Deeply embedded in Vitruvius's discourse is the home, where the "mistress sits surrounded by her weavers" in a Greek-style villa and where the male landowner entertains guests.[9] This is not the architecture of everyday life but the architecture of a small class of people who can afford the beautiful proportions the architect achieves by using his extensive knowledge to subject the base building materials to the ministrations of an abstracting hierarchy.

The world Vitruvius proposes is one in which arrangement is everything. He arranges the city according to a pseudoscientific interpretation of the landscape, prevailing winds, and soil conditions. The building arrangement follows rules of proportion that are supposedly derived from the male body. The pieces of the building then interpret that body in the structural logic of stone that was first developed by the Greeks. Within this armature Vitruvius and his followers lay out the rooms according to another pseudoscience, that of function.

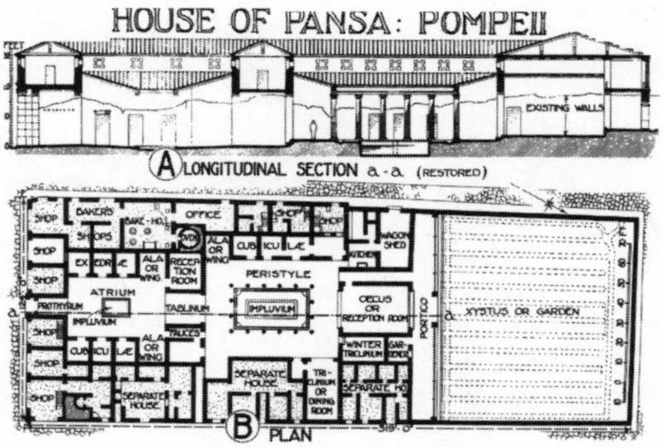

Figure 3.4: House of Pansa, Pompeii, c. 150 B.C.

By generalizing specific acts or needs, like sleeping, eating, or entertaining, the architect can tame them with reproducible forms. My body at rest becomes contained in exactly the same way your body is, and the thing that contains both of us was planned and constructed before we used it, and it will survive us. Its cold reality is stronger than our frail occupation. This act of arrangement finally buries or imprisons the activities of daily life and the woman who is at the heart of this. It also excludes everything that is not completely arranged, everything that is not made out of stone, everything that cannot be known, everything that does not belong.

By defining architecture in this way, Vitruvius severely limited its realm and opened it up to internal contradiction. Since it has nothing to do with the lives of anybody but the ruling class, and finds its highest expression in the idealized and removed religious structures that represented Roman culture, it could not partake in helping people shape their daily lives. Since it tries to make everything inside it conform to principles laid on by an architect and derived from sources far removed from the actual building material, body, or activity, it must continually struggle to control and suppress the reality of life. This struggle causes architecture to become ever more intricate and ever more severe in its ordering devices. Columns, walls, divisions of wall surfaces, and specialized spaces proliferate, as does the ornament that is meant to weave them all together, to the point where architecture either becomes a complete artifice that has nothing to do with life or becomes, as Vitruvius himself feared,[10] so complicated that it dissolves into the complexities of everyday life.

The architecture of Rome was pure order. It was the order of the crossroads and the order of architecture itself as a professional citing and siting. The Forum in Rome, itself both a Greek agora and crossroads, was the heart and the embodiment of that order. Ringed by little temples and objects that contained the places of gathering and the wealth of the Roman state, it was a place of appearances, where the various attempts to perfect the architectural order of the temple form vied with one another for attention. Emperors later reproduced this empty space in the vast courtyards and proliferating rooms of their palaces or enlarged it to vast spaces where activities and violence turned into self-referential games, the arenas. The rest of the population, meanwhile, lived in densely packed apartment buildings, or *insulae,* where the interior world of the woman and the poor person was reduced to the barest minimum it took to survive. Dotting this landscape of emptiness and condensation were the axes, the obelisks, and the temples that represented imperial power.

Only one type of structure offered an alternative to this order: the bath. The bath started out as a simple place where one could undress, remove all the orders of the world, and cleanse one's self. It was a place to rediscover the body and to immerse one's self in nature. By the time of the establishment of imperial rule, however, it had become a gathering space that offered an alternative to both the rigid formality of the public houses and temples and the

Figure 3.5: The Forum, Rome (reconstruction), c. 100

·49·

Figure 3.6: Sir Lawrence Alma-Tadema, *The Baths of Caracalla*, 1899

emptiness of the Forum. It was a slightly misty realm, a place where you could discuss politics and where people gossiped. There was a rhythm and ritual to the place, defined by the three baths (a *tepidarium,* or a room with a lukewarm bath; a *caldarium,* or a room with a hot bath, and a *frigidarium,* a room with a cold plunge), but this was a sensual order focused around a square filled with flows. The architecture of the baths, by the time it was elaborated into such grand palaces of ablution as the Baths of Caracalla in 217, was one of great vaulted and domed spaces that proliferated in seemingly endless sequence of connected spaces, through which one flowed with ease. This was not a world of columns and pediments, of proportions and abstractions of the human body. This was a world of curves, flows, and sensuous delight. It became the place where people—including women and some poorer people—gathered around a kind of perverse mirror image of the campfire, the pool of water. To this day baths serve as oppositional gathering points where ad hoc communities are created.[11] This was the other side of Roman architecture: the side of the arch, which the Romans invented, which grew out of the ground and encompassed space in an infinite manner. Made up out of humble bricks and creating the vast structures of the baths, the arenas, and the aqueducts, this was the architecture of gathering. Unfortunately the arches crumbled and the society fell apart, while the underlying grids remained to define cities for centuries to follow.

Rome also created its own counterspaces in the villas of the wealthy. On one level these were little fragments of Roman order that colonized the countryside. The cataclysm of Pompeii has preserved the essential Roman villa for us. Based on the Greek model, it is a series of colonnaded rooms grouped around a succession of courtyards, each more private than the one before it. Beyond the public rooms of gathering and appearance are the private apartments, where life is lived in small cells. Beyond the walls of the villa, the villa owner colonized the land for agricultural purposes, allowing him to convert the legal ownership of land into concrete wealth and food and becoming a model for seigniorial control.

The villa is also the Roman order strained to the breaking point. As the villa grows, it becomes a labyrinth, a series of open spaces in which you have to know your way or your place in the elaborate domestic ritual in order to find the place assigned to you by the arrangements of this domesticated architecture. And those cells, those places of privacy where you are not a citizen participating in the affairs of state, come alive with painting. Nature returns through the back door, in painted form, as frescoes that turn the inside into the outside, that dissolve the order of the wall, that animate space into overlapping, fantastical orders.[12] In frescoes, columns don't always hold anything up, rabbits skip across tile patterns, and things in general fall apart into fragments, evocations that are only faint echoes of sense and arrangement.

In the Roman villa the first real interior emerges. Here, finally, we can see an interior that is not merely that which walls happen to enclose or that is the result of the needs for certain functions or the place of mystery where only the goddess and her priests live. This is the space that we inhabit, that offers a space mentally outside but physically within the rigid orders of architecture, and that dissolves those orders into places of comfort and fantasy. To the Romans these were slightly dangerous places, places of sexuality as well as sensuality, where the male order could break down and perversion could set in. They were the spaces of women.[13]

There were, of course, very few such interiors. For all the beauty of the frescoes unearthed in Pompeii, for all the tiled floors that brought a natural world into the heart of villas in England and Tunisia, the villa remained mostly a bleak and imprisoning place to women and a small part of an order that was oppressive to all those who did not have access to its fantastical realms. Wealthy women lived in isolation, covered up and controlled by men, even if they did often have more power than Greek women. The only temple that represented them was the circular form of the temple of the vestal virgins.

Yet one can argue that the orders of Rome that fixed in absolute relationship the place of women and the place of men in an architecture of exclusion and inclusion show us that the reality of life will continually undermine such alien forms. Even the emperors themselves dissolved their own grand designs. When Nero built his palace in the heart of Rome after the fire he might have helped start or not have prevented from spreading in 64 A.D. he took the imperial ambitions of his predecessors one step further by razing a whole

Figure 3.7: Garden Room, House of the Wedding of Alexander, Pompeii, before 79 A.D.

·52·

neighborhood and erecting his own palace in its place. It was one of the first great aptly named gentrification (built by the gentry) projects in history. Yet what amazed the citizens of Rome, beyond the sheer willfulness of this move, was the fact that in the place of the small apartments the palace replaced was not just built space but endless terraced gardens. These domains of pleasure replaced the reality of urban living with a fantastical nature, complete with representations of all the major cities in the empire, mechanical springs, artificial flowers, gold mosaics, and metal birds. Nero had brought urban civilization to its head. His control over people's lives was so absolute that he could will them out of their places of existence. That embodiment of power was nothing but a void that tried to mirror the nature that the city itself had destroyed. After order comes only fantasy, and the Golden House was a realm of pure fantastical sensuality.[14]

Ever since then the final embodiment of male imperial power, the power to control the universe completely, has not been just the edifices in which this power is exercised or lived but the great emptiness it can open up. The power of building is also the power to negate and to assert the naked, controlling line as nature or natural. This was the case in the geometrically arranged terraces and axes of Nero's domain, and this was the case with the gardens of Versailles and all the other quasi-natural domains of pleasure that potentates throughout history have imposed on the world they controlled.

These are places of power that are hard to define in terms of use or even in terms of reality. In them the real space of experience dissolves into the pathways and borders that define the beds of planted material.[15] The only enclosure, or expression of vertical difference from nature, is actually made out of growing material, so that you have to maintain it with great diligence lest it dissolve into what it seeks to mirror. The garden or landscape, which means, in the Dutch word the English adopted in the realm of William and Mary, "shaped land," is a place in which man's desire to replace nature is not buried within objects of use but is asserted plainly and delightfully. Ironically, it is also a place where, as we shall see later, power is, in the eyes of Western civilization, feminized.[16]

At the heart of Nero's particular power play was his throne room. It revolved around a circular, domed space covered in gold leaf, where all reality finally dissolved into nothing but the monochromatic, dazzling reflection of sheer aura that became the "space" on which the figures of Byzantine art floated for centuries after. It was said that in a state audience the emperor would appear as if out of thin air with the help of a mechanical throne and a great deal of smoke and fireworks.[17] This was the epiphany of imperial power, a technological feat that produced an ephemeral result and, in so doing, shaped space with absolute results, as from this golden room the decrees that controlled every aspect of daily life in the Roman Empire emanated.

The arc of Roman space leads from the crossroads and the codification of the rules of architecture as abstract orders imposed on the activities of everyday life—the expression of a male order—through the proliferation of these rules and spaces and their spread through much of the Western Hemisphere to a kind of decadence in which they dissolved into man-made nature. They became spaces of artifice, where order disappears into a second, man-made nature. This was the final apotheosis of the fragmented, artificial pleasure worlds of the villa interior and its increasingly complex, experiential orders.

This is an arc of power that was to repeat itself in Western civilization. It has been given a stylistic slant by art historians who have noted a progression from primitive to classic to baroque or elaborated and finally decadent, rococo, and neoprimitive forms.[18] One might note, however, that we can also see this progression as the establishment of an artificial order over the real world, its elaboration, and its dissolution in the emptiness that underlies that whole act. It finally leaves us free to wander in a completely artificial, empty world without purpose or order that is as far removed from the real world as one can go without entering another plane of existence. It is at this point that art historians speak of an art and architecture that are feminized, it is at this point that the clear divisions of power give way to the weavings of court politics, it is at this point that the communal (within the group in power) delight in sensuality takes over from the acquisition or production of either space or other human beings. It is the space that Gilles Deleuze has called that of "retroactive smoothing,"[19] in which the hierarchical planes of artificial space and the vertical erections of a new world dissolve back into the flows of nature.

In the case of Rome the spaces of opposition came both from without and from below. The spaces that ran counter to the *cardo* and *decumanus* were the swaths of destruction that broke through barriers of defense and ignored the order of the field and the roads of communication. They were created by the nomadic tribes that swept into Europe in successive waves after the third century. The world of the tent reasserted itself, showing how tenuous the culture and spatial divisions of Greco-Roman civilization really were.

The space of the Goths was the space of the tent, but it was also the space of negation, the smoothing of the hierarchies of Rome back into an undifferentiated space. Significantly, in at least one of the tribes, that of the Celts, who ruled England before the Roman invasions, women held equal power with men.[20] Certainly the art of the Goths was not the art of building, nor was their statecraft one of fixed laws and exclusionary statutes. Rather it was the art of metalsmithing, the continual testing of material at the point where it changes state and the elaboration of the tools of cutting and destruction into a weaving of an alternate world; and the world of weaving itself. As such it was an art that disappeared, rather than leave many traces of monumental achievement.[21]

The social structure of these nomadic tribes, based on the confederation of different clans and a fluid interpretation of events so that the group could respond to new lands and new technologies with great ease, was one that similarly did not have the staying power of Roman laws and thus is difficult to define. Yet the spaces created by this culture were so powerful that within a few generations they had laid waste to the edifices the Romans had spent centuries building up and had replaced them with spaces of flows that the people themselves continually had to reweave into a new culture.

Figure 3.8: Catacombs of Via Latina, 4th century A.D.

This process of weaving a culture back together became the great task of the early Middle Ages. The threads that provided the material for the tapestry that eventually created the skeletal explosions of the age of cathedrals came from small bands of underground communes in which women played a significant part. The catacombs, the Christian cell, and the monastery became the proto-type for a new kind of social space, a new space of culture, that gave us a rich flowering of arts before it was buried in the crypts of those same cathedrals.

The catacombs were the first oppositional spaces of which we have any record. No doubt such places of refuge existed in many other cities in the male-dominated Mediterranean universe, but the ultimate success of the Christian sects that gathered there led to their partial preservation. First, the most significant aspect of these spaces was that they were not contained in buildings. They were places of gathering that were cavelike. They were originally spaces carved out of the earth themselves. Just as the early Christians refused any pretense of worldly power, so their spaces removed themselves from the confident erection of images of power and containment. Instead they created interiors without exteriors, rounded spaces, and spaces of passageways or tunnels that connected, rather than lead to some grand and final event. Out of necessity, these spaces were nonhierarchical, so that if one piece was discovered, it did not compromise the network of interconnected spaces.

Figure 3.9: Nave, St. Etienne, Vignory, 11th century

Since these were spaces removed from the normal light of day, they were places where people created an artificial version of the everyday life through painting. They painted the deeds of the Bible as if they were the elements of daily life that they consecrated through ritual: bread and water. It is easy to overromanticize such spaces. They were dark, dank, and dangerous, and no doubt the actual social structure of the early Christian communes was not nearly as truly sharing and ahierarchical as the church itself liked to make out. Yet they offer a countermodel to the rigidly functional, layered spaces that spread out above them, and by tunneling under the foundations of the ordered grids of columns and axes and the artificial emptiness of the forum and the gardens, they managed to help transform a whole society.[22]

As soon as the Christians came to power, they abandoned these spaces and the communal and antipolitical forms of organization that they had developed there. The church was built as a new form of temple, as hierarchical, axial, and ordered as the pagan edifice out of which it, in the case of most early churches, was constructed. In this world neither women nor spaces of flow had any place. Only in certain aspects of the Byzantine

Figure 3.10: San Vitale, Ravenna, c. 540

exile did the oppositional force of the catacombs survive: in the rounded forms of the basilicas, in the plain and woven form of the paintings they pieced together from a myriad of little glistening tiles instead of applying them with broad brushstrokes, and in the very real power exercised by many of the early empresses. The Church of San Vitale in Ravenna is a model of what the religious institutions of Europe could have looked like. The basilica is an agglomeration of curved surfaces that has no real facade, no axial progression leading anywhere. Instead the church dissolves into a series of overlapping places of gathering that together both buttress and help form the central spiritual gathering point. That space was a place where you could dissolve into the splendor of a new world under a dome of heaven that dissipated the troubles of everyday life into a tapestry of spirituality.

In the West there was the crypt. The crypt was a place carved out underneath and within those orders, a space of roundness, of niches, of carved-out corners and elliptical roofs, a place where space could be unpredictable and even happenstance. It was a space for the dead, those people who had escaped the rigidity of a secular order. It was a place without light, where instead of what you saw, it was what you believed in that mattered. It was a place of magic, of darkness, of the earth, and of cults that started out by preserving the power of the original spirits of the place and then developed into the incubation ward for the huge cult of Mary that swept Europe after the plagues, crusades, and other disasters of the twelfth century,[23] bringing in its wake not just a serious

Figure 3.11: Crypt, Monastery of Holy Luke, Greece, 10th century

challenge to the secular and religious authorities in the form of spiritual sects such as the Cathars, Albigensians, and the Spiritual Franciscans but also a revival in a culture connected to the crafts of the home.[24]

In the early churches outside Italy a counterworld survived in the form of the crypt. This was not only the place of burial but the place where another world was posed against the rigors of the real world aboveground. The crypt was the place that represented the presence of a heaven in which all hierarchies and the spaces in which they realized themselves disappeared. The crypt was also the place, curved and domed, where quasi-pagan cults survived, just as the cult of the goddesses had survived in the hidden domestic recesses of the cities of Mesopotamia.

The crypt stood to the spaces of everyday life in the same way that the temple or church stood to the edifices of secular power. The church was the vertical assertion of male power, revolving around the adoration of a male god and arranged according to the same rules of predictable structural and aesthetic order. Walls were subdivided by pilasters, bays were defined by columns, and a central axis led up to the throne of God or the altar. The church was a place of light and order, a place in which the community knew its place. The emptiness of the space opened up below and in front of the consecrated area where men clothed themselves in the albs of appearance and removed wealth from consumption by claiming it as holy chalices and the other treasures of the church.

Overhead the spire or spires proclaimed the power of this place, transforming the structure of columns into single statements that were both the symbol of a community's heart—not a hearth but a point that could not be occupied— and the primary point of paranoia, since it was from here that the community learned of danger through the tolling of the bell.

The history of church architecture from the early temples and basilicas of Rome through the simple, warehouselike spaces of the truly Dark Ages into the more elaborate structures of the Romanesque and the great exaltations of the Gothic cathedrals, a history that seems to be the mainstay of most architectural histories, is no more than the recitation of the complication of these few simple principles. As the church becomes less and less a place for hidden cults and less and less a place of communal defense, it becomes more and more subjected to a visual and structural logic that creates more and more empty space and layers an ever more complicated architectural language over the space of communal gathering.

If the edifice of the church represented the spiritual perfection of the systems of order present in the other institutions of a male-dominated and repressive state, then the crypt was the spiritual version of the home. It resembled the simple rooms, hovels, and bare bones enclosures in which most people lived and in which the woman was both imprisoned and acted as the organizing force of the household. We, of course, knew very little of these spaces. They were often made out of the material at hand, such as clay or twigs, and thus returned to the earth as soon as they were no longer occupied. They certainly were not places where people spent much time by choice. They went there

Figure 3.12: Holy Trinity Church, West Sussex, c. 1020

because they were cold or hot, to eat or to sleep, not to revel in the artificial world they had created:

> Into the twentieth century, wherever they lived in Europe, peasant women had one large central room, anywhere from 5 to 25 meters long, about 4 meters wide, with one section for people and one for animals. The building would be one story, sometimes with a sleeping loft, sometimes with rooms added at the end of the house when an aging mother and father had given over the land to daughters and their husbands or to their sons. They covered whatever windows they had with translucent substances like waxed cloth, horn, or cut talc. In warmer climates, there was no covering, and they simply closed the wooden shutters when colder weather came.[25]

Figure 3.13: Pol van Limburg, *Winter,* from *Les Très Riches Heures de Jean, Duc de Berry,* 1415

What we do know about these houses is that in northern Europe the confinement of women to the home loosened up. Whereas in the Middle East the tradition of *purdah,* or confinement, institutionalized the segregation of women into the home, and in southern Europe the confinement of women continued the traditions of the Greek and Roman *gynacaea,* or women's rooms,[26] to the north there appears to have been somewhat more flexibility. Women moved more freely through streets and in some cases continued to hold some of the power that had been theirs in the days when their ancestors were still nomadic. There were no designated women's spaces, but then there weren't any spaces only men could inhabit.

This greater flexibility of space derived at least partially from the lack of public space in the settlements of northern Europe. As historians such as Georges Duby have pointed out, the Middle Ages were a time of privatization.[27] The impersonal structures of the state that the people of northern Europe inherited from the Romans gave way to the personal bonds of vassalage. Instead of the forum or agora, instead of the rambling order of the palace or the interiorized worlds of the villa, instead of the crossroads, early medieval society revolved around the fortified farm or fortress and around the community meeting space of the church. These structures were not places where public man appeared and defined himself through languages and laws that were far removed from daily life. They were places where local chiefs could hold court and decide on immediate affairs. They were often hearths or movable thrones set up in the cavernous hall of the fortress. The larger courts did not tie themselves to any given place but continued nomadic traditions by traveling between fortresses. They carried the furnishings that allowed them to give shape to and inhabit the otherwise undifferentiated caverns of the stone fortifications with them.

Thus a tradition emerged in which buildings were essentially places of defense, storage, or communal gathering, while it was furnishings—the crafted goods such as tapestries, chairs, beds, small storage chests, and cooking utensils— that actually defined and made livable space. There were few of these goods for the poor, and more for the rich, but the division remained the same. The result was that there were two kinds of spaces: the space of order, permanence, defense, and communality, which was the space controlled, defined, and built by men, and the space of sleeping, eating, conversation, and other ways in which relations between people became real, and these were as often as not defined by women.

The space of men was the space of the wall. It was a vertical space of redoubts and ramparts, turrets and hilly places. It was a space that did not have a human scale. It contained spaces with little differentiation and was a place where the man always played a role or appeared. For poorer men, it was the space of the village square, the space of the social gathering, the space where they erected an alternative world. It was a place to be somebody, not to live or open yourself up to experience.

Figure 3.14: Donjon, Houdan, c. 1100

Women's space snaked itself through these walls and voids of appearance. It had little physical or permanent reality. This made women's space as ephemeral as the goods that created it and as real as the routines of everyday life. The only definite space was the space of the bed, which sometimes became an enclosed space within itself, and the kitchen, which was not much more than a relationship between technological implements around the hearth. Women's space became the space created by the relationship between the all-purpose spoon and the face, the horizontal space of the bed with its layers of covering, the space of the hearth where the family gathered for warmth and food. It was a space woven together by use. These spaces disappeared into use and embroidered beauty out of use.

As the Middle Ages progressed, these spaces were formalized in the courts of the rich, and the production of these tools of everyday life was removed from the domain of women. Whereas crafts such as weaving had in the eighth and ninth centuries been almost exclusively the domain of women, and women had helped produce many of the goods they used to maintain their families, by the fifteenth century the emergence of guilds that purposefully excluded women began to remove from women the power to shape their space through these goods.[28] At the same time, as the urbanization of northern Europe became more rapid, women found the sphere of the home more and more hemmed in by the needs of defense, which constricted the space of the city, and by the orders of streets that male rulers increasingly carved out of the city. The space of women became the streets and the market space, the place of connection where women could weave relationships with one another. The space of men became that of the wall, the palace, and the other institutions of law and order.

It is from this period that we can date the formalization of the space of women as the domestic sphere. It is the space inside, the space of domestic furnishings, the space of family relations, the space that is not recorded or represented. It is the invisible, always changing, flexible, and sometimes even comfortable space of everyday life. The space of men is the space of appearance, of violence, of order and judgment, of ritual. It is fixed, monumental, and outside daily life.

This does not mean, however, that the two sexes lived in completely separate spheres. Unlike societies of purdah, women and men were segregated only in the highest classes, and even there a great deal of fluidity appears to have existed. Men and women met in the marketplaces, on the streets, and in their homes. They partook of many of the same joys and trials. They simply lived together. Yet women lived in a world that men produced for them, into which they had to fit themselves. They experienced the world as given and their spaces as a continually flexible response that existed only as long as they were able to act within the space of men.

·63·

Figure 3.15: Anonymous, *A Knight Visits His Lady,* 15th century

4

THE ROMANCE OF OTHER SPACES

WITHIN THE DARK SPACES OF THE MIDDLE AGES two places of change emerged.
The first was the isolated space of the monastery, abbey, or Beguinage; the
second was the world of the court. Both were realms where women thrived, if
only in carefully circumscribed situations. Both still survive today, though much
transformed: Abbeys, nunneries, and the girls' schools that derive from them
were until recently the only avenues through which women could partake in the
forming of our culture, while the world courtly literature enshrined became the
highly "feminized" world of the baroque court and then the ritualized middle-
class home world.

Both the institutions became models for a better society. The abbey became
the prototype for the school, the commune, and other institutions that were
meant to transform society. From the monasteries of the Middle Ages came
the inspiration for colleges, boarding schools, academies, and professional
schools. These were idealized communities of learning where social relations
were strictly regulated for the purpose of rationalizing both the individuals
that attended the classes and the society as a whole. The tradition of the in-
stitution of learning as a model and incubator for a better world in turn af-
fected how we have thought about building a better place. Rather than imagine
that we can change the way we live every day or that we can merely make

our cities and countryside places of more justice, beauty, and comfort, we have tended to think of self-enclosed communities. Utopias have often been not sprawling urban spaces but compact buildings that presented their idealized lives in the form of perfectly proportioned spaces and carefully controlled systems of entry. The monastery or school became the model for an earthly paradise.

The world of courtly romance, on the other hand, was a rarefied place. It was far removed from the process of conquering, contesting, and filling in the landscape of Western Europe. While the men were out fighting to make the world safe for Christianity, the plow, and the production of goods, the women of the upper class were locked in the castle. Their only avenue of creativity was to invent an alternative world to the one they could rarely see. A fantasy world, filled with good manners, good design, and men who were solicitous of their needs, replaced a reality in which they were the property, interchangeable with horses and gold, of "real" men. The logic of the court was that of magic, its driving force was a narrative without end (the quest), and its aesthetic was that of soft, colorful surfaces and rounded phrases. This, too, was a kind of utopia, a good place that existed outside current conditions. It also had its own rules and logic, embodied in the way in which it appeared. Against the rigid formality of the scholastic utopia, it offered the ephemeral world of shifting appearances, tapestries, and secluded, hidden bowers. If the scholastic model tried to adapt the masculine definition of the good, the world of the court presented a countermodel of a good place as women defined it, on the basis of their experience. They turned their confinement into a place of beauty and offered it as a model.

What made both of these models so powerful was that they had qualities of what the French philosopher Michel Foucault has called heterotopia. The heterotopia, as Foucault describes it, is a kind of mirror we hold up to our society. It is a place "in which all of the real arrangements, all the other real arrangements that can be found within society, are at one and the same time represented, challenged and overturned."[1] What Foucault has in mind is a place that is familiar, that we use every day, but that has properties that remove it from everyday life, while changing our perception of the world outside the heterotopia. In prisons, cemeteries, schools, hotels, camps, museums, and theaters, another version of the world appears. It is one that is more logical and more organized but also filled with possibilities that do not exist outside these controlled environments. In theaters and museums time either stops or is sped up. In barracks social relations are organized into rigid rules that are mirrored in the Spartan settings of these communal sleeping areas. In colonies or ships a whole version of a regular community is set adrift, compacted, and reorganized.

There are six principles to these heterotopias. They represent points of crisis, when we must confront our bodies or our psyches in transition. They have a system of opening and closing that defines their realm. They have their own time. They change as society changes, so that they continue to mirror the aspirations and fears of the community. They juxtapose a refined version of the world with the reality of use. Finally they allow another, unreal world to appear: "On the one hand they perform the task of creating a space of illusion that reveals how all of real space is more illusory, all the locations within which life is fragmented. On the other, they have the function of forming another space, another real space, as perfect, meticulous and well-arranged as ours is disordered, ill-conceived and in a sketchy state. This heterotopia is not one of illusion, but of compensation. . . ."[2]

The importance of heterotopic spaces is that they are places where we can understand our society in a different way. In a theater we can literally restage reality. In a school or barracks we can enter into social relations, wear uniforms, and engage in rituals that make the world a much clearer place. In cemeteries, museums, and other places where time stops we become aware of our quality as part of a world of objects and spaces, instead of convincing ourselves that we have a special reality only apprehended through the senses. On the other hand, the heterotopia is that place where we make our mental maps real in sensual delight or horror. It is this quality that links such heterotopias—as the special huts in which many societies have isolated women during menstruation or men during puberty—and the world of the theater and the museum. In the heterotopia we see ourselves as real, but we appear as part of an artificial system, one in which we are clad differently or behave according to a script. The artifice of human culture becomes blended with our sensual reality to the point where we can isolate the structure of our culture and remake it. A museum can open up new worlds for you, but so can a school or a cemetery.

I would contend that it is women who have in our society created, nurtured, and often controlled heterotopias. They had to. By the twelfth century, when both Beguinages and courtly romances began to flourish, their realm had been limited for more than two thousand years, and whatever cults or systems of kinship they had kept alive within the militaristic realms of men was increasingly coming under attack. The Crusades turned into the massacres of the Albigensians and their cults of male/female power.[3] The formalization of traditional nomad law into written precepts coordinated according to Roman jurisprudence left little room for the *ad hoc* decisions and accommodations from which women had often benefited.[4] At the same time the steady spread of an agricultural society that provided significant surpluses and the trading system it produced created a wealth, leisure, and culture that allowed women the freedom to define their world.[5] The only place where they could do this was either in the world from which they excluded men—namely, the monastery—or in the world in which men shut them up.

The great double monasteries of the eighth century provided the first place in which women could exercise any power. Several of them were run by powerful abbesses who could even resist the wishes of bishops and kings. These wealthy fortresses of faith were, like their male counterparts, places where the arts, both practical and aesthetic, were cultivated.[6] As such, there was not much that would allow you to distinguish them from their male counterparts; this was, of course, one of their most remarkable aspects. Both monasteries and nunneries were places of strict order, where the day and all its activities were tightly regulated and every activity had its own meaning. This meant that order and meaning, or significance, came not from some abstract rule or idea, as it would in a church or in a palace, but out of the activities of everyday life. In the monastery the very act of eating, washing, tilling the ground, or writing was meant to be a tribute to God, and thus it was endowed with a meaning it did not have outside the walls. Those activities in which women engaged, such as cooking, weaving, and cleaning, were done by both men and women, and at least ideally, no activity was to be valued above another.

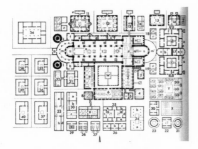

Figure 4.1: Monastery of St. Gall, c. 820

Figure 4.2: Abbey of Cluny (reconstruction), c. 1157

One can see this order in the structures themselves. Great abbeys, such as Cluny or Clairvaux, were horizontal sprawls of different, specialized activities.[7] They did not focus on church spires, had little useless open space, and had no hierarchical divisions. There were no grand axes, no squares, no important and unimportant buildings. There were only the different shapes, sizes, and materials that might be appropriate for eating, weaving, or praying. The large indoor spaces, such as the refectory, had little of the axiality, the sense of rhythm of structure that would reinforce the grandeur of the space. Even their simple detailing tended to weave stories across surfaces rather than define what was meaningful and what was not. These spaces were open, had simple walls, and were light and bare. Nothing in that space told you what to do; the activity itself informed the shape of the space.

The outside appearance of the buildings furthered this sense of simplicity. Rarely were there any symmetrical facades, any columns or friezes that told you what was important about the space. Instead of squares, circles, and rectangles, the monastery was often made of fragmented geometries such as semicircles, reflecting the breakdown of abstract order in favor of the needs of the monks and nuns. What order did control the design of these structures was, according to the founder of the Cluniac order, Bernard of Clairvaux, derived not from geometry, the stars, or any laws of proportion, but from the body of Christ, which was both the body of (desexed) man and the body of the community.[8]

In fact, the work of construction, the work of everyday life, and the work of praise were one with and in these spaces. These heterotopias were real spaces, but they were also places where there were no great deeds and spaces made by and controlled by men and no dark, insignificant spaces in which women created everyday life, but only the organized, artificial, simple, fragmented, sensuous world of a Christian community. That means that they were egalitarian places where women's and men's work was to make a better world—not as an abstract, pie-in-the-sky activity but as a real place that every good Christian could inhabit. These communal structures were real models for a better world.

These communes reached their apogee in the humble structures called Beguinages. Unlike the abbeys, the Beguinages were usually urban structures inhabited not just by wealthy women but by women from all classes. They sprang up in the late thirteenth century in the Low Countries and quickly became popular places where widows, younger daughters, or women who wished to escape from the bounds of male society could find a place to live and work. The nuns of the Beguinages did not engage in a great deal of either agriculture or the kind of social work, such as tending to the sick or helping the poor, with which nuns of other orders became associated. Instead they became famous for their simple ways of life and for their embroidery and weaving. The Beguinages of northern France, Belgium, and the Netherlands were centers for weaving craft. They were places where the emerging industries that were to turn these areas into the economic powerhouses of the next few centuries became acts of significance.

The structures of the Beguinages were as humble and as functional as the activities that took place inside them. Often they were hard to distinguish from the homes around them. They were more orderly and flexible versions of the domestic realms that surrounded them. Filled with light and a variety of spaces at different scales, they were somewhere in between the home that was the domain of the mother and wife and the communal utopia that was the place of the nun or monk. They wove the fabric of the city together and transformed it into an alternative version of what an urban community might look like. To this day Beguinages continue as places where women can create their own space.[9]

Figure 4.3: Refectory, Fountains Abbey, 1135

To some religious women, such a world was not enough. They sought to escape from reality and enter another world. The writings of the female mystics of the twelfth century are startlingly different from those of their male coun-

Figure 4.4: Beguinage, Ghent, c. 1250

terparts. The female mystics wrote prose that abounded in images of harmony, unification, and diaphanous splendor. As Caroline Walker Bynum has pointed out, "Women's religiosity was less characterized by conversion and inversion; their sense of self or Christ as physical stressed continuity between their social and biological experience, on the one hand, and the experience of encounter with God, on the other."[10] Thus "Almost exclusively female are: miracles in which the recipient becomes a crystal filled with light, miracles in which the recipient distinguishes consecrated and unconsecrated hosts . . . and miracles in which the Eucharist has a special effect on the senses."[11]

The most famous of these mystics was Hildegard of Bingen, who could write such prose as:

> In the year of our Lord 1141 when I was forty-two years and seven months old, the heavens opened and fiery light throwing off great streams of sparks utterly permeated my brain and ignited my heart and breast like a flame which does not burn but gives off heat the way the sun warms an object which it touches with its rays. And suddenly the meaning of the Scriptures, the Psalter, the Evangelium and the other catholic books of the Old and New Testament were revealed to me. . . .[12]

The female mystics all emphasized the dissolution of the bounds of their bodies and of the real world, erecting instead layers of revelation in which all dissolved into pure light. As noted above, this mysticism has both deep roots in cults of female deities and a long history in female mysticism. In the twelfth century it also helped feed the rebellious doctrines of the Cathars. Its beauty lay in the splendor of the world it imagined as existing beyond reality, and it continues to offer a strong antidote to the laborious constructs of church-based scholasticism that constitute the mainstream of church doctrine. To men, women represented the carnal reality of everyday life, or *anima*, while the man, with supposedly higher reasoning power, was the spirit, or *spiritus*. One can imagine that these associations come out of the role to which women were assigned—namely, daily housework and child rearing. The church failed to see that it was exactly the ability to transform the everyday into the perfect that set women mystics aside from a church that had to cordon off a special place and ritual in order for salvation to appear. Women kept alive the transformative, metaphysical nature of place and body.[13]

What we might term the feminization of religion, including the Mary cult and the various mystic strains, even echoed in the structures that contained and gave place to faith, tended to ever-greater ephemerality. Some of the greatest cathedrals of northern Europe managed to dissolve the rigid hierarchies of faith into a sexless ideal world. In a cathedral like that of Beauvais what matters is not so much the vertical thrust of the columns as the proliferation of members, so that it is difficult for the eye to trace the order either of gravity or of geometry. Thirteenth-century innovations, such as the fan vault, covered the plain ceilings with a pattern more reminiscent of fabric than of stone. Glass took over such large expanses that the boundary between outside and inside, between the real and the fantastic (or holy) almost disappeared. If one can imagine these great structures painted in lavish colors, so that every surface became just another facet in another layer of the stone tapestry, one can imagine that this was a space of liberation. In the church you could form a community, you could escape the confinement of your body and the position in which class and gender had put you, and you could weave yourself into the texture of ideality. The rose window became the *mandala*-like summation of another ideal but uninhabitable space.

·71·

Figure 4.5: Nave,
Sainte-Chapelle,
Paris, 1243–48

Even the outsides of these imposing structures tended to disappear. As the structures became increasingly elaborate, they lost the clarity of the simple rectangular Romanesque structures. The radiating chapels dissolved the center, the proliferating aisles diffused the central axis, and the stone carvings covered the central facade. Where the building did impose itself, it was soon buried beneath

Figure 4.6: Cathédral Saint-Julien, Le Mans, 1194–1230

houses and stores that wove it back into the texture of the city.

The cathedral was not a feminine space, nor was it a real space you could inhabit every day. It was, however, a place that offered an alternative to the rigid structures all around it. The height of Gothic architecture, represented by such cathedrals as those of Chartres, Amiens, Beauvais, and Salisbury, threatened to dissolve the rigid orders into layers of ritual, magic, decoration, and ephemerality that could have drowned the rigidity of the male order that had created it. In this sense it is tempting to read the twin developments that stopped this from happening—namely, the stripping of all decoration by the reformation and the replacement of the Gothic forms with neoclassical and baroque architecture—as an attempt by male architects and male rulers and thinkers to reassert their power over the world, a development that we shall explore further in the next chapter.

In the everyday life of at least the richer women another fantastical world appeared. The world of the courts shares much of the imagery of the mystics but used it for much more immediate purposes. The romances were, of course, written by men (though a few women became proficient writers),[14] but the world they described was one that women controlled to a remarkable degree. This was a direct result of the inclusion of women (in the sense of sequestering them) that became a status symbol among Western European courts starting in the eleventh century. The wealthier a nobleman was, the more he could afford to keep his women out of harm's way. This was not just an idle idea. The wife of a nobleman often represented a major investment in dynastic allegiance, paid for with a dowry. She was supposed to produce an heir that would ensure the continuation of that investment.[15] There was a real danger that the woman could be stolen from his control, an echo of the primeval wife stealing that Lévi-Strauss believed ensured the vitality of clans at the dawn of civilization. The woman was, and still is, mobile as well as changeable, a piece of movable furnishing or wealth that had to be controlled by the heavy walls of the castle.[16] The redoubts, walls, and other defensive measures of these fortresses were thus meant to keep the women in as much as they were meant to keep perceived enemies out.

The first fact of the wealthy woman's life was thus that of imprisonment. We can easily imagine that the spaces in which she found herself locked were at first as bare, undifferentiated, and uncomfortable as the hovels of the poor or the storehouses of the fortress itself. The castles were, after all, initially no more than fortified encampments for what remained a somewhat nomadic class. As the mores and rituals of the castle became more developed with the blossoming of

Figure 4.7: Nave Ceiling, Gloucester Cathedral, 1370

the medieval economy, women began to decorate these spaces with increasing vigor. The first such decorations were obviously the tapestries that kept the cold out while recounting the great deeds of the men (such as the Bayeux tapestries), but these were soon followed by a profusion of furnishings. Though these were generally made by men, women often dictated their use and decoration. They already controlled the "home" or space that the men occupied when they were not at work or war. Men commented on the comforts of home with both fondness and a certain condescension. The idea that there could be a value to comfort, to sitting in a comfortable chair, to storing goods out of sight, or even to being warm was at odds with the strict hierarchy of values that placed the great deeds performed by warriors at the pinnacle. In general, they (and thus law and economic relations) valued the outdoor activities of men, whether it be trade or agriculture, far above the work of cleaning, cooking, and child rearing performed by women.[17]

Figure 4.8: Anonymous, *Philistines Carrying the Ark to Azotum,* Cathedral, Anagni, c. 1255

The most characteristic aspects of these furnishings were always the tapestries, curtains, and veils that served to define the spaces of the interior. Whereas stone walls and wood frames might have created the actual enclosure, it was

Figure 4.9: Anonymous, *The Happy Citizens of the City of Ladies,* from Christine de Pizan's *The Book of the City of Ladies,* 1450

often the same material that had originally made the nomadic tent that created the interior divisions within these large forms. Tapestries turned the walls into evocations of other worlds, where human figures, animals, buildings, and trees interlaced themselves along the lines of the thread, creating a collage of colors and forms that dissolved the harsh realities behind them. Between the walls, curtains and veils cordoned off certain areas reserved for specific uses. In some of the earlier castles only such permeable barriers defined the private area of the lord. These curtains ranged from the heavy cloth that could create a clear seal for heat and noise to the flimsy gauze, often imported from the East, that was much prized for the way in which it created the sense of richness while making these desirous objects even more tantalizing by obscuring them. The curtains were often drawn around such carefully defined spaces as the bed, which was often no more than a wood contraption with a curtain spread over it.

Inside the castle, in other words, the tent survived. It was a place of changing spaces, of everyday activities defined by movable, richly decorated, comfortable, and sensuous materials. The tapestries and curtains both brought other worlds into the space and defined a certain space, creating places of fantasy and secrets. It was the world in which the child was first born, it was the world of nurturing, and it was the place to which the man returned after he had done his great deeds to lead his perhaps not so significant but very real life. It was a space of women.

More remarkable than the world of tapestries and curtains that women spun through the dark halls of the Middle Ages was the world of fantasy they created within those spaces. Starting in the twelfth century, those halls began to echo with the sung and recited stories of knights, damsels, loves, and grails. Taken together, these stories both continued to embroider on the spaces invented by the nomadic groups and the Romans and became the basis for much of Western literature. The romances contained a limited amount of variables, in terms of structure and in terms of narrative development, and thus mirrored the spaces of the castles in which they were recited. Like the tapestries, however, they wove an elaborate world out of these elements.

A secularized version of heaven on earth, and specifically around the hearth, abounds in such poetry. Take, for instance, the following tenth-century song:

Figure 4.10: Anonymous,
Bedroom, from *Les Heures
Boucicaut*, c. 1375

> Come, sweetheart, come,
> Dear as my heart to me,
> Come to the room
> I have made fine for thee.
>
> Here there be couches spread,
> Tapestry tented,
> Flowers for thee to tread,
> Green herbs sweet scented.
>
> Here is the table spread
> Love, to invite thee
> Clear is the wine and red,
> Love, to delight thee.
>
> Alone in the wood
> I have loved hidden places,
> Fled from the tumult,
> And crowding of faces.
>
> Now the snow's melting,
> Out the leaves start,
> The nightingale's singing,
> Love's in the heart
>
> What boots delay, Love,
> Since love must be?
> Make no more stay, Love,
> I wait for thee.[18]

Certain spaces keep recurring in the romances. There is the cave in which the treasure is buried or the knight encounters the monster. This primeval space is a little like the Greek *chora,* a sexless, inhuman space of beginnings or confrontations with the all. Its opposite is equally absolute: It is the world of heaven, the vision of translucency where all forms melt into radiant colors. Such spaces might anchor the beginnings, transition points, and ends of the romance, but the real work happens in the bower, the glade, the bedchamber, or some other hidden space.

These are the spaces in which nature has been woven into a controlled environment, whether figuratively by the writer or literally in the case of the man-made chamber or garden. They are places of secrecy, of culture, of dialogue, where action takes place through words, not deeds, and where the only reality is that of the textures woven by such words and the women who speak them. They are the spaces of love, not war. Such spaces are places of connection, relationships between people, desire, union of bodies, sensuality of the skin or its surrogates, and all the ritualistic inventions we create in order to contain, communicate, and organize such emotive realities.[19]

These are spaces of beauty, and that beauty is essentially ephemeral. Woman's space here becomes both the space of fiction and the space of fashion.[20] On the one hand, it is an imaginary space that is hard to define exactly because it has little corollary with the "real" world. Since women are imprisoned and caught in days of daily rituals and lives in which their only function is to provide sexual pleasure and heirs, they create an alternative world where none of these constraints exist. In these magical worlds one can be in many places at one time, whether in the heart of the knight out on the quest or in the dreams of another. Time and space collapse, allowing passion to weave alternative connections and divisions. The secluded garden is a place where love and even sex can flourish. On the other hand, how one appears in these literary visions is the most important matter, since one often is only an appearance. As Georges Duby has pointed out:

> . . . the dream house eventually ceases to be regarded as a reflection of heaven. Three main impressions emerge from the most significant texts. First, the ideal house required an enclosure. Indeed, as the thirteenth century approaches, the population density inside the castle walls decreases; the court becomes a setting for individual exploits. Second, the ideal house was highly eroticized in these literary works composed for "youths," that is, unmarried males. It is depicted as a female preserve; women are watched, kept under lock and key, which makes them only more alluring. The towers are filled with maidens. Here we glimpse the recurring fantasy of free love—repressed and turned into a myth of origin . . . here, however, the fantasy has pejorative connotations. In courtly romance, whenever the game of love is given an explicit

setting and the hero breaches the castle walls to seize a woman, the adulterous union tends to take place underground: making love is not something done in the open, and when that love is illicit, it must literally bury itself. Third, in the profane imagination the ideal house was light and airy: a thousand windows flooded every obscure recess with light. Further embellishing their image of the house, writers threw in souvenirs of the River Orontes, glimpsed on a Crusade, as well as Turkish art, fountains, and ornament of every sort. In imagination, heaven was a superb castle filled with people, and the ideal house was a dazzling paradise fitted out for the joys of life.[21]

It is from this period that date the seemingly contradictory images of the woman as part of nature and as artifice, as virgin and as whore. The space of the woman becomes the space of the garden, something natural to which man must return from sex but which he has caught, walled, and domesticated. Within that constraint the space of the woman is luxurious, organic in its blossoming, rounded and intertwined in its shape, and attractive to all the senses. The woman is a rosebush, the garden itself; she is landscape, the part of nature that man has re-created. She is also the womb, the bearer of a secret space within her that a man can never enter, but out of which he somehow appears. Again, he can control the body but not the space of growth inside it. This makes that hidden, secret space both an object of desire and something to be feared.

Man has thus found a space for the woman. He no longer needs the gynaeceum, the purdah, or the other physical spaces of seclusion. He grants the woman three spaces: the space of her womb, which becomes the space of the home; the space of the garden, her own version of nature contained and re-created by man; and the space of her own imagination, which is also the space of magical or ideal appearances and thus, eventually, the space of fashion.

The last of these spaces is the most ephemeral and the most heavily identified with a specifically feminine culture. From the Greeks to the present day, women have reserved the arts of clothing and weaving for themselves and have created the shelters, comforts, and beautiful patterns that allow us to live in the harsh orders created by men. It is, however, by its very nature not a

Figure 4.11: Anonymous, *Garden,* from the
Chevalier de la Tour Landry's *Book for
the Instruction of His Daughters,* c. 1190

space that gives a great deal of stability.[22] It is a space that is radically disconnected from the woman's body since it is about covering and converting that
body into an appearance that corresponds, at least ideally, to a mental and fictional image of the woman: the woman as seen in the mirror; the woman that
is an object of desire; the woman that is the rose.

The garden would seem to ground the woman back in her original role as
gatherer of the products of nature, but it is essentially unproductive. The garden becomes the image of nature that is almost by definition useless, at least
until late-eighteenth-century romantics try to bring the park back under culti-
vation. The garden is a place where flowers appear to sight, smell, and touch
only. It is a place of labyrinthine forms, of intertwined branches, and of natural shelter but one that does not provide shelter, that ultimately has only a
limited set of orders, and that is pruned and controlled by gardeners. Like the
space of clothes, it is a space of artifice.[23]

The same is obviously true of the space of fiction. There real things happen
in real spaces, but they are only facsimiles, copies of such a reality. The space
of fiction is the space where appearances and control meet to create an alternative narrative to the activities of everyday life. It is another world, but a
world that one cannot inhabit, a space in which one can be only literally, not
actually, at home.

The identification of women with artifice, re-created nature, fashion, and fiction is something that flows not from their innate nature, their connection to
the chthonic, or the fact that their bodies are rounder but from the position
in which men put them. The feminine artifice is a counterspace set up against
the orders of man.

This feminine space of artifice and intrigue became an architecture of its own
in the châteaus of the Loire. Though based on fortresses, such structures as
Henri IV's Chambord were caricatures of defense. Their turrets had become
circular shapes that bowed out with the uses inside them and provided no ramparts from which to defend the castle. Their roofs had turned into collages of
chimneys, each leading to a circle of warmth and comfort inside, and their

many gables reiterated the message (and reality) that this was a series of home-like spaces, not a singular defensive structure. Rising like a mirage in the middle of an artificial forest, it was a compact agglomeration of moments of sensuality and comforts, so complex that one could easily get lost in its rooftop labyrinths and endless little rooms that opened up to one another around the central, ceremonial halls buried deep inside this fantasy structure.

The doubled, helical staircase at the front of the main building summed up this fantastical landscape. Neither inside nor outside, it doubled its function, thus giving lie to the very notion of functionality. It was constructed out of a profusion of curves that turned in on themselves, twining themselves around a profusion of slender columns. This spiraling space was the space of intrigue, where you could pass each other, see each other, imagine from the other person's appearance what he or she was doing, but where you could not actually do anything about what you saw. This was a space that never began and ended, that refused the boundaries of building and of fear, that opened up endless possibilities and gave itself over to a joyful artifice.

Figure 4.12: Staircase, Château de Chambord, 1519–47

Such palaces of artificial pleasure proliferated only in a small area and for a short period. Their only equivalent was the space of the masque, a ceremonial performance, usually based on mythological or biblical narratives, in which the whole court would be both actors and spectators. These performances, which blossomed in the courts of the Italian city-states in the sixteenth century, were lavish affairs in which costumes, flowers, stage sets, and even fireworks all worked to create a space of artificial appearance or illusion. It is interesting to note that the men and women often played interchangeable roles. These ephemeral spaces were often designed by noted painters, architects, and composers—including Dürer and Inigo Jones— and allowed them to try out some of their more fantasy-ful ideas.[24] What is

Figure 4.13: Antonello da Messina, *St. Jerome in His Study*, c. 1450–55

more important, however, is that they also tied into the tradition of masqued balls, carnivals, and other communal celebrations in which the rigid, male-defined orders of class and gender were given temporary space. During carnival the city is another space, a fantastic version of itself, a heterotopia that erupts out of everyday life and then disappears behind the brooms of the women who have to clean up its debris.

In the same period the permanent structures of gender became more rigid. Several architectural historians have pointed out that one of the first specialized spaces to make its appearance in the urban homes of the rising merchant class was the Italian *studiolo,* or study. This was the man's own secret space, a male version of the woman's chamber. Like the woman's room, early versions of this space, such as the 1450 studiolo of the duke of Urbino, was covered with fantastic evocation of another world. Unlike the woman's room, however, this fantasy was made out of wood, and the space was defined by strict grids. Even more important, this was a space not for living but for storing and working with the legal documents that defined ownership of the house and for writing the correspondence that placed the home in an economic, legal, and social structure. The study was the place that became the microcosm for the orders man imposed on the world. It was the place where man stored the tenuous and abstract ciphers that bound that order together—documents that were as cold and difficult to understand as the tapestries of women were sensuous and evocative.[25]

Beyond the study, the home became ever more specialized. Instead of one large room in which a family or clan could eat, sleep, socialize, and do whatever else defined their communal life, there now appeared a profusion of separate rooms. In French and Italian, these specialized spaces were called a *chambre* or a *camera,* as opposed to the multipurpose *salle* or *sala.*[26] Each room had a particular function, but some functions were more important than others. Thus the kitchen remained, and remains to this day, the most undifferentiated space, the one most dominated by technology. In this space the woman continues to weave connections between utensils and ingredients with little need of anything other than ventilation, fire, storage, and work space.

The dining room remained equally large and undifferentiated. It was essentially a public space, where the handicraft of women became a product that both satisfied hunger and displayed wealth. The halls in which men conducted business or held court were even more dominated by the rough orders of stone and wood, though these spaces might become more and more elegantly proportioned and decorated. In contrast, such spaces of extreme privacy, such as bathrooms, when they started to appear, were undecorated, meaningless holes in the fabric of the house.

Figure 4.14: *Studiolo* of Federico da Montefeltro, Palazzo Ducale, Urbino, c. 1470

It was the gradations from private to public that became the subject of ever-greater elaboration. First, separate bedchambers appeared. Next, the wealthy needed receiving rooms and dressing rooms. As time went on, these rooms proliferated. If a woman could once receive special visitors in her bedchamber, by the late sixteenth century she had a special room of appearance, a reception room. To prepare herself for these activities, she needed a dressing room. Then she needed a withdrawing room, where she could wait or into which she could disappear at the appropriate moment. Nor was this true only for women. Wealthy men needed an equal progression of spaces of appearance. Thus the *levée,* the ritual rising of the king that had become a major court ritual by the time of Louis XIII of France, resulted in a series of specialized rooms that mimicked the coming into appearance and thus the emergence of power of the king and eventually led to the need for such giant expressions of radiating royal power as Versailles.

At first glance such interior specialization would finally seem to give woman a space of her own, but the reality was somewhat more ambivalent in its effects. These were not spaces a woman made for herself but rooms that reflected an elaborate ritual of appearance that was imposed on her. It was up to the woman to make these spaces her own, and the amount of space she had to fill, of course, allowed her to fix herself in ever more and more beautifully crafted pieces of furnishing and tools of the toilette. Wealthy women could indeed create empires of their own in these rooms, exclude men from them unless they followed the rules of etiquette, and decide the shape and activities within the walls. Yet the more elaborate these spaces became, the more women were imprisoned in them. The interior became even more the only place where the woman belonged and where she was lost in her own sensuous labyrinth.

Moreover, such spaces were a reality only for the very wealthy. The effect of specialized spaces for poorer women was more devastating. The growth of cities, the increased need for imposing, monumental structures for the rich, and the expansion of spaces of production and consumption such as factories and stores, put a tremendous pressure on the amount of living space available to the poorer classes. While public space increased, whether in the form of open squares or as ever more elaborate ramparts, boulevards, axes, monumental buildings, and other spaces of male order, the spaces of living actually decreased.[27] Cramped, badly ventilated, and crowded with an ever-growing population, the living spaces of the late medieval and Renaissance city, those spaces where most women were confined, became increasingly dismal.

5

IN 1500 AN UNKNOWN CENTRAL ITALIAN ARTIST created a vision of a perfect city. A fountain stands in the middle of a large open space. A grid of granite in different colors covers the plaza and continues off into the distance, where it merges with the frame of the painting itself. Within the grid stands a series of buildings. Each is a perfect object. One is round, one is octagonal, and two are severe cubical masses. They all are built out of what looks to be marble. The few people who dare venture out into this daunting environment are tiny, as if they have been squashed down by the buildings. Everything is in its place, everything is balanced, and everything is empty. There is no sense of an interior to any of these buildings, no sense of life or movement around them; there are no stores, no carriages, no sheets hanging from the windows. Only at the center of the background does a triumphal arch lead from this scene of perfection to what might be a real city, a place of brick and different scales. The new world is rising in front of us, and we can only admire its alien beauty.

Nothing moves. The architecture is there. It stands; it controls; it is. You might say that the buildings have taken over for the life of the people. This is the ideal world to which the ruling men of the Renaissance aspired. In this world the activities of everyday life were of as little importance as they were to the Greeks. What mattered was the perfect order they could create in place of both nature and those lives.

Nobody ever built this world, but its image dominates most architectural thinking to this day. While this world could only be painted, every building had to aspire to build a fragment of it and could be judged by how well it neared that ideal. Everything else had to be subordinated to this effort. Even if the precise form of this ideal might change from one made up of columns and domes to one made up of arches and steep roofs or, in our century, to one of flat roofs and white surfaces, its unapproachable silence remained. Its power has made it difficult for women to make places of their own without arguing that they can create such sterile and grand voids as well as men.

Figure 5.1: Anonymous, *Ideal City*, c. 1500

In the Italian Renaissance the project of art and architecture became the creation of an ideal and unreal world. It was a world that reflected and made real the increasingly rigid and rational world that was subjecting all of reality to its organizing forces.[1] The world of Galileo, Machiavelli, and later Giambattista Vico and René Descartes, where all humanity is subjected to law, order, and the empty systems of appearances,[2] became the world that art wanted to make real.

To do this, it needed rules. In 1486 the Italian theoretician Leon Battista Alberti created the first great codification of how one should make and control space since Vitruvius's *The Ten Books of Architecture*. Alberti's *De Architettura* is one of several treatises he wrote as handbooks for aspiring artists.[3] Central to all these texts is a system of values and spaces connected, as the art historian Svetlana Alpers has pointed out, by the notion of visual control.[4]

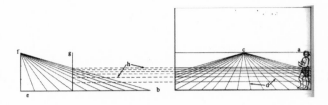

Figure 5.2: Leon Battista Alberti, *Perspective,* from his *On Painting,* 1435

The operative image in this system is the window. The window is, first of all, a frame for a system of perspective. Perspective was one of the great innovations of Renaissance art, and we usually see it as a method for more faithfully rendering three-dimensional reality on a two-dimensional surface. It was much more than that, though. Perspective was essentially a grid that the artist placed over reality to subject it to an ordering system. The grid, which Alberti suggested you create by stretching strings within the frame, gave everything and everybody a place. It dissected reality into series of squares and thus removed them from reality.[5]

This meant that the value and reality of all things depicted existed in the grid itself and no longer in the objects. In fact, Alberti and other Renaissance painters claimed that the reality they were creating was better, more ideal, and better organized than the one that they were subjecting to their art. As Leonardo da Vinci said:

Figure 5.3: Albrecht Dürer, *The Artist and the Reclining Woman,* 1525

Whoever loses sight, loses the beautiful view of the world and is as one who is shut alive in a tomb wherein he can move and live. Now, do you not see that the eye embraces the beauties of all the world? It is the master of astronomy, it makes cosmography, it advises and corrects all human arts, it carries men to different parts of the world, it is the prince of mathematics, its sciences are most certain, it has measured the heights and the dimensions of the stars, it has found the elements and their locations. It has predicted future events through the course of the stars, it has created architecture, and perspective, and divine painting.[6]

The window was the perfect image for this conceit. The world the Renaissance artist depicted was one that existed at a remove, out there, beyond touch, smell, or taste. You could not inhabit it but only see it. Similarly, the completed painting was itself a window into another world, one that again existed by virtue of the gaze. The result was that this was a world that existed only through the craft of the painter. It was essentially fictional. Unlike the fictional world of women, however, it did not come out of sensual experience, nor was it one that everyone could partake in. It existed only either as the raw material for the artist's order or as the finished product of the painting, which was to be perfect and so well glazed that one should not be able to see the brushstrokes that would betray the craft. The painting and the world it represented were mental products that came into being by subjecting material to abstract laws and led to an image that existed out there, beyond use, beyond touch, in the world of ideals.[7]

Alberti justified this ideal product by giving it an ideal project. According to Alberti, the aim of painting was not to represent reality but to tell a story. This was not to be just any story either. Rather it was to be an *istoria,* a tale of great deeds that had occurred in the mythological past. Only these deeds were worthy of the talents of a truly great painter because in that way he will "move the soul of the beholder."[8] Thus what went on in daily life was of no interest to the painter. The history he was to write in paint was to have a moral lesson and was to teach the viewer to behave. In Alberti's scheme, painting becomes an annex to or an embellishment of writing. It is a more convincing set of marks that connects the laws and mores of the land to reality through the eye.

Alpers calls this the art of expression, as it assumes that there is something that exists beyond what we can know through the senses. Whatever that is, we can only understand it—which is to say, we can postulate a deed, truth, or space that could exist beyond the one which we inhabit but of which we can have only signs, whether written, painted, or built.[9] The ideal world Alberti and his fellow theoreticians postulated could by its very definition not be inhabited. It could only be seen, imagined, or evoked.

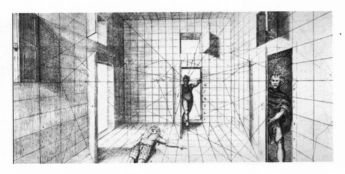

Figure 5.4: Hans Vredeman de Vries,
Perspective, 1604

What was an architect to do if the model for his activity was the window that presented a nonexistent world out there, beyond our reach? He should be able to translate those ideals into a built reality. The architect was for Alberti, as he had been for Vitruvius, a gentleman whose task was to make the world fit for the actions of great men by bringing the full force or reason and abstract logic to bear on this manly task:

Him I consider an architect, who by sure and wonderful reason and method, knows both how to devise through his own mind and energy, and to realize by construction, whatever can be most beautifully fitted out for the noble needs of man, by the movement of weights and the joining and massing of bodies. To do this he must have an understanding and knowledge of all the highest and most noble disciplines. This then is the architect.[10]

To do this, the architect had to know the "lineaments" or good lines of buildings and its structure. Architecture was a question of aesthetics and science, married in proportions and appropriate form. In all this Alberti was doing no more than following Vitruvius. He only goes into much greater detail on matters of site selection, materials, working methods for the designer, and uses of ornament. Alberti is writing for a gentleman architect, a man who needs practical and aesthetic advice on how to create a pleasing and sturdy surrounding.

The building will work and be a good place only if the architect meets all the demands for security, sense, and proportion, if he follows a recipe that removes as much choice and authority from the act of construction or living as possible. Beauty, for instance, is something necessary:

Figure 5.5: Andrea Pozzo,
Doric Column, c. 1693

Beauty is that reasoned harmony of all the parts within the body, so that nothing may be added, taken away, or altered, but for the worse. It is a great and holy matter; all our resources of skill and ingenuity will be taxed in achieving it; and rarely is it granted, even to Nature herself, to produce anything that is entirely complete and perfect in every respect.[11]

What is missing is any sense of life. This is a world that is "perfect in every respect." To Alberti, beauty is not in the changing vagaries of life but in the way the trained eye of the beholder finds abstract principles that are usually not even visible. This is a place that makes sense only to a gentleman of taste.

Even the useless appendages of ornament have a separate place and book. They are meant to bring out the lineaments of the building, to catch the eye and make it realize what really matters about the building, and to convey why the building is important. The ornaments are not sensuous, not beautiful in their own right, not a commentary on a building. Ornament is thus completely subsumed into the overall building process, as the natural result of the use of abstract principles of proportion, structural logic, and functional apportionment:

> In this case, unless I am mistaken, had ornament been applied by painting and masking anything ugly, or by grooming and polishing the attractive, it would have had the effect of making the displeasing less offensive and the pleasing more delightful. If this is conceded, ornament may be defined as the form of auxiliary light and complement to beauty. From this follows, I believe, that beauty is some inherent property, to be found suffused all through the body of that which may be called beautiful, whereas ornament, rather than being inherent, has the character of something attached or additional.[12]

Ornament is a way to mask reality, even when it permeates a structure. For Alberti and most architects after him, a building could and should be reduced to its necessary components. These are the great, noble, and manly elements of architecture. However we live within those forms is secondary. To make the whole more palatable, we need ornament—something added, something over and above the absolutely necessary, that allows us to understand and enjoy our life in the building.

Certainly for most architects this added material was like the woman, no more than a pleasant addition. Architects needed it to make a history of noble deeds into a real life. It thus helped to fix the notion of femininity as a category of

·89·

male values. The feminine was a supplement that hid the reality of structure, its use and time—all the other qualities with which women had become associated because of their exclusion from the realm of significant deeds and which remained unspoken, unsung, and unbuilt.[13]

Nowhere does the role of women and femininity become clearer than in the images of the Vitruvian figure produced by a series of architects in the first half of the sixteenth century. They were illustrations of Vitruvius's claim, at the beginning of his third book, that the male figure, if he stretched out his arms and legs, could define both a perfect circle and a perfect square in abstract space. Leonardo drew the most famous illustration of this text. A naked man, his symmetry adulterated only by the stance of his feet, creates the overlapping figures. There are numerous other examples of this figure, however. Francesco di Giorgio and Fra Giocondo, for instance, both created less compelling versions. All agreed that the circle stood for the world as a whole, as complete as God had made it, while man then squares this condition with his body to allow him to stand in and fill out that world.[14]

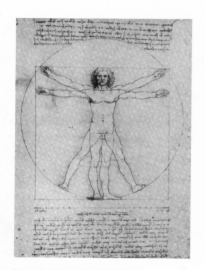

Figure 5.6: Leonardo da Vinci,
Vitruvian Man, **1507**

It is in the 1521 version by Cesariano that the sexual overtones become explicit. Cesariano believed that domestic architecture was inferior to the creation of monuments and that architects were demigods.[15] His version of the Vitruvian man has an erect penis. The circle here is the undefined, abstract and preexisting. It is the eternal, the all-encompassing, and, by implication, the feminine. Cesariano made the square not just with four lines but with a grid, as if it were Alberti's perspectival window. The male figure is impregnating the female circle to produce the square that reproduces endlessly and produces a new order in which even the male figure is caught.[16]

There is no doubt that the architecture of the Renaissance was one of order. You can feel it in one of the early monuments of that era. Designed by Brunelleschi, the Hospital of the Innocents in Florence, finished in 1445, creates an empty space surrounded by precisely molded arcades, as if the ancient stoa had turned in on itself, merged with the monastic courtyard, and refined itself into a simple, static space. Nearby Brunelleschi in 1482 divided Santo

Spirito Church in Florence into equal bays, each a structural and visual component in an overall, harmonious whole that is white, filled with light, and devoid of any but the simplest ornament. Alberti himself, when in 1472 he designed the Church of Sant' Andrea in Mantua, used the Roman triumphal arch for the facade of the building. Not only did this solve certain compositional problems—namely, how to blend the peaked or vaulted space of the nave into the flat presentation of the building as an ideal object—but it also meant that when you passed through the arch, you were entering a kind of new Rome that was a place of order and another world. Inside, the space was immense, singular, and overwhelming. Coffered grids stretched above bunched columns, as if the muscles of the church were holding on to the geometrical world it was creating.

Figure 5.7: *Vitruvian Man:*
a) from Francesco di Giorgio, Codex Ashburnham 361;
b–c) from Fra Giocondo's edition of Vitruvius, 1511;
d) from Francesco Giorgi, 1525

The 1434 Duomo in Florence was similarly a triumph of engineering and visual composition that created a perfectly harmonious and static environment. It was a perfect *mandala*, a figure of the universe condensed into a singular object where it could be inhabited, known, converted by ritual into a lived experience, and removed from any sense of reality. In 1510 Bramante condensed this form into the little *tempietto,* a perfectly round building sitting in one of the courtyards of the Vatican. It had a dome that was almost feminine in its roundness and proportions. It was the symbol of the world, surrounded and held up by columns. Looking at the *tempietto,* you can see the feminine circle abstracted and removed from any connection with real women and contained by male erections.

Great palaces, such as the Palazzo Farnese by Sangallo (1515), transformed the defensive home into a geometric figure, in which each room was a subdivision of a larger proportional game. Instead of rambling and specific compositions that responded to needs for entry, for keeping out the rain or enemies, or to the activities inside, these rooms were fragments of a pattern of stone,

Figure 5.8: *Vitruvian Man,* from Cesariano's edition of Vitruvius, 1521

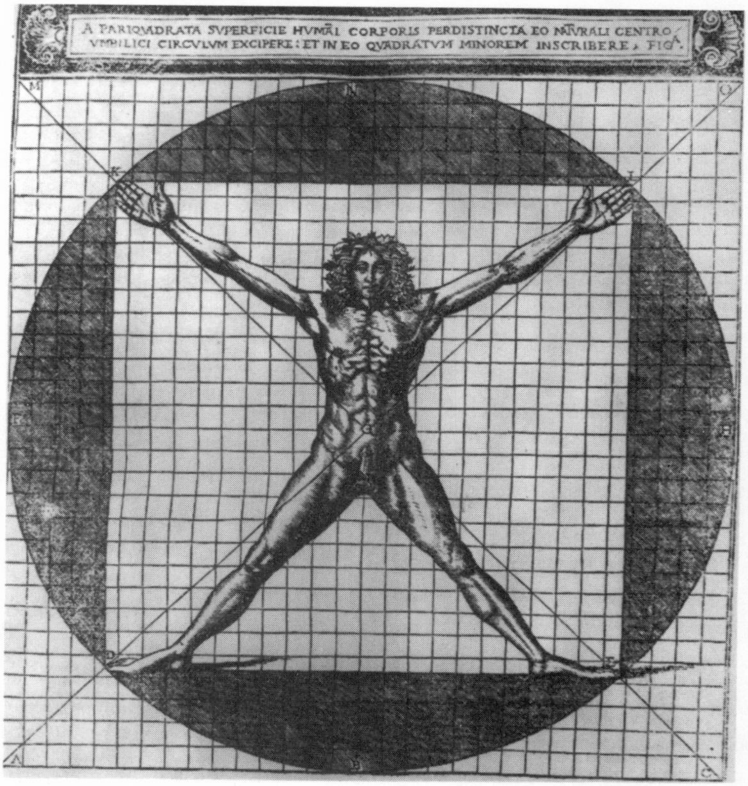

columns, lintels, cornices, and windows that repeated themselves without regard to what went on inside them or around them.

The palace of the Medici, the most renowned family in Florence, was similarly just a facade that gave a series of connected row houses a common facade. It subsumed the shops and storehouses of this rich clan in a base of rusticated stone, marking these places of work as being part of a roughhewn foundation, something somewhat closer to nature. Above that the *piano nobile,* or formal floor, was the space where the columns were the largest, the stone was the finest, and all the proportions came together. These were the rooms of appearance, where the clan held court. Above that the small windows got lost in the ornament. This was the place of real life, where the bedrooms and ancillary spaces were found.

Andrea Palladio, who wrote his own book on architecture, took this tendency the furthest.[17] The Villa Rotonda of 1552, for instance, was one of several summer places he designed for the wealthy noblemen of Venice in the countryside around Vicenza. The villa is completely symmetrical around two axes. Its central space is a rotunda. Each room is a proportional subdivision of the overall block. The block sits on top of a hill, looking out over its domain and containing within itself a perfect world.

Palladio popularized his method of dividing all rooms up into pieces of a constructional puzzle through line drawings. What these drawings left out were the furniture, decoration, and even direct painting that converted these idealized spaces into working places. In the Villa Rotonda, for instance, the Venetian painters Agostino Rubini, Ruggiero Bascape, and Domenico Fontana filled the main hall with evocative paintings that transform this perfectly proportioned space into a whirlwind of colors, scales, and textures mixing classical vistas, tempestuous skies, and voluptuous bodies.

Many of the villas were in actuality working farms, their courtyards filled with hay and horses. The ideal of the Renaissance existed in books and in the minds of the architects, but the reality of these visions was one in which ornament, furniture, and life took over. Architects such as Alberti and Palladio designed great structures, taking care to follow a logical process and to maintain a harmony of all parts to one another so that nothing could be taken away without harming the overall building, and then painters, decorators, and clients came and hid all this work. To the architects, painting, sculpture, and furnishings were of secondary importance. They were what came later, what softened the lines, what made them appealing. They belonged to the realm of women. To the inhabitants, these elements were exactly what made the grand gesture into a real, inhabitable space.

Figure 5.9: Filippo Brunelleschi, Santo Spirito, Florence, 1446

Figure 5.10: Leon Battista Alberti, Facade, S. Andrea, Mantua, 1470

Figure 5.11: Michelozzo di Bartolommeo, Palazzo Medici-Ricardi, Florence, 1446

Figure 5.12: Andrea Palladio, Villa Rotonda, Vicenza, 1550

Figure 5.13: Agostino Rubini, Ruggiero Bascape, Domenico Fontana, Hall, Villa Rotonda, Vicenza, 1550

It is amazing how many of the great buildings of the Italian Renaissance were actually skin jobs. The greatest spaces of all, the courtyard of St. Peter's, designed by Bernini in 1657, and the Capitol, created by Michelangelo in 1546, were no more than layers of classical architecture that hid the confusion of perfectly functional construction behind them. The Capitol is an empty courtyard that has no particular function. Michelangelo's facades unite three separate bureaucratic structures by giving them echoing orders of columns, lintels, and arched windows. At the heart of the square the emperor Marcus Aurelius points off to the distance from atop his horse. A man engaged in great deeds occupies the center. He is a sculpture, a monumentalized version of a real person. Michelangelo similarly idealized the world all around him .

In front of St. Peter's, space has become even more removed from reality. Columns that rise four stories create a grand scale. They are not just facades but a whole structure that is meant to do nothing more than screen out the city and create a forecourt for papal power. Hundreds of poor families were forced to move to make way for this gesture. At the center of this court sits an obelisk, a trophy from faraway Egypt that acts as a phallic marker of pure power.

Though facades such as these denoted the relationship between real life and appearance, they also marked a severe split between the outside or appearance of things and the world on the inside. The same Renaissance that gave us the great build-

·94·

ings of Alberti, Brunelleschi, Bramante, Palladio, and Michelangelo also gave us a new cult of domesticity. The cult of the Virgin Mary was transformed from an adoration of a queen of heaven into a portrayal of a voluptuous woman holding a real baby. Fat, colors, and curves were everywhere in the round medallions and portraits. Domestic scenes appeared in paintings. We can see the Virgin Mary lying in bed when the angel appears to her to announce the virgin birth. We can see the scholar in his messy study, the saint in his deathbed, the holy family with animals gathered around them. This means that we can study the furniture, the tools, and the spatial relationships of everyday life. That life now has a place and a representation, even if it is only as background to the great deeds of dead men. Architecture and painting cannot be empty. They start to fill with real life.[18]

Figure 5.14: Michelangelo, Campidoglio, Rome, 1546

·95·

This is not designed space. This is the space that just happens between the columns and the walls. This is not space that is fixed. It flows from scene to scene, often without clear borders. This is a space that has a human scale, in which the chairs, beds, and chests have the same color, texture, and size as human beings, while the blank geometries of the architecture tower over them. This is often a very real world that almost seems to mirror the world around it. It is a world that is introspective, that focuses tightly on the woman and her child, on sumptuous materials, and on the gaze from one figure to another. This is a world of intimacy.

Men quickly made a place for this world. In 1537 the architect and theorist Sebastiano Serlio published his *Seven Books on Architecture*.[19] In it he described the correct stage sets on which one can reenact all important activities in the world. He presented these stage sets as the places where a person can look at his or her world and understand what it means. The first and the most important stage set is the one that is appropriate for the enactment of tragedies. These are the dramas that matter, that follow the classical rules of unity, that tell the stories of important mythological figures and have a strong moral les-

Figure 5.15: Fra Filippo
Lippi, *Madonna and Child*,
1452

son that reminds us that all real life is only illusionary and that death and the retributions of abstract justice are all that matter. The space of law and order is one of columns, perspective grids, proportional windows, and symmetries. It is stark, clear, and clean.

The space of comedies is, by comparison, a mess. It is a collage of buildings of different scales that poke up in front of one another. Where there are columns or window surrounds, they are incomplete and have no relationship with one another. There is no clear order, no hierarchy, and no logic. There are, however, many opportunities for people to hide, to shout at one another, or for surprises to occur. This is the world that mirrors real life and transforms it into an insignificant but enjoyable place where importance is shrugged off with the latest misfortune.

The most interesting scene is the third, or satiric (and satyr-ic), scene. This is a scene of nature, a forest with a lane running through it. The trees function as columns, providing a regular order to the whole. Yet they are also alive, branching out into complicated patterns that obscure one another. This is the realm of fantasy, where satyrs live and things might not be what they seem. It is the place where meaning and farce shade into each other, where appearances become reality and vice versa, where change and transformation, or metamorphosis, are the order of the day.

The tragic scene is the scene of architecture. The comic scene is the scene of everyday life. The satiric scene offers the possibility of another place, one where architecture and real life might mix as fantastical nature. It is the space of the garden, which in the Renaissance became an extension of the order of the villa or palace but also became the place where the woman, as in the medieval romances, made her presence felt. It was a place of magic and sexual liaisons. It was a place where order broke down. In drawing all three scenes, Serlio was encapsulating order, its lack, and the escape from it all within a system that gave importance to the first, realized that the second existed, and opened up the possibility for something that traveled between inside and outside, the man-made and the natural, the real and the unreal, the masculine and the feminine. Unfortunately the fact that they did so only in the

Figure 5.16: Sebastiano Serlio, *The Tragic Scene, The Comic Scene, The Satyric Scene,* from his *Seven Books on Architecture,* 1551

grand structures of power meant that the real space of daily life, the world defined by women, was left out of the diagram.

It was only the tragic scene of architecture that moved north across the Alps into France, England, and Germany. Only monumental forms and pure orders were exported as tools by which rulers could control their reality. There these colonies of perfection had to confront the reality of everyday life all over again. When they became so grand and all-encompassing that they stifled their inhabitants, they dissolved into the garden and fantasy. As was the case with their Italian models, they operated only for the very rich and relegated architecture to its position as the translation of power into built form.

Nowhere is this vision of French space embodied better than in the Château of Vaux-le-Vicomte. Finished in 1661, this vast villa and garden complex was the realm of the powerful minister of finance for Louis XIV, Nicolas Fouquet. It embodied every principle of the new, rational nation-state which was able to control all production, whether agriculture, manufacture, craft, or art, through laws, regulations, taxes, appointed inspectors, and often direct ownership. Vaux-le-Vicomte was a microcosm of the whole world subjected to rational control. The compact stone mass, designed by Louis Le Vau, showed no memories or notions of defense. Nor was it merely a facade. It was a solid block, its bays divided by thin pilasters. As you approached it, it stepped back to accept and overwhelm you. A steeply sloping roof replaced the hidden tile roofs of the Italian Renaissance palaces, serving to give the building even more weight. At the center a dome rose like a basilica from behind a grand pedimented porch. The dome mirrored a round reception area, where the guest would find himself finally removed from the direction of his travel and spun around into the perfectly sequenced spaces of reception and ritual that filled the main floor of the villa. All was order, clarity, and weight. It was a place that captured the line of travel and released the visitor into a new world.

The gardens behind the château were that liberated space. Stretching out toward a nearby river, they stepped down in a set of low terraces, so that their breadth increased as they spread out in front of the viewer. The great landscape architect André Le Nôtre designed them to be thin, almost ephemeral planes. A wide gravel path and a canal continued the central axis of the main building all the way down, past a symmetrical pair of outbuildings, past the empty lawns and shallow pools of water, to a circular fountain that reiterated the shape of the dome. Here Le Nôtre completely emptied the artificial forest that Fouquet had planted around Vaux-le-Vicomte, replacing it with a vast emptiness anchored by a condensed container or ritual. Everywhere the eye roamed, it found only parts of this perfect and empty world.[20]

There was a place for people here, of course. In contrast with the rigid lines of the landscape, they were meant to come careening up to the house in their carriages, sweep through the formal rooms, and stroll through the gardens. The human figure and its unpredictable actions were the only thing that enlivened this architectural framework. This was the great achievement of French baroque architecture: to empty the scene of everything but the constructed frame and the main actors. Le Vau and Le Nôtre had created the perfect scene, an artificial world that did away with any preexisting reality.

Louis XIV was so impressed by this achievement that he put Fouquet in prison and asked Le Nôtre and Le Vau to redesign his hunting lodge in the small village of Versailles into the center of the universe. Joined by the interior designer Charles Le Brun and such talented furniture makers as André Charles Boulle, they brought Renaissance principles of architecture to their logical conclusion. Here man became not just an unpredictable actor but a sun-god apotheosized—a principle of absolute order made flesh. The king rose every morning at the center of the axis that split Versailles in the middle, stretched his arms like the arms of the building that opened up to receive visitors from Paris in a series of ever-taller and more widely spaced pavilions that forced a sense of intensity on the center of the palace, and issued forth his commands through a bureaucracy that became ever more complex and diffused as the palace moved out from the central cabinets of state to the myriad apartments of the functionaries, dignitaries, noblemen, and courtiers who filled out the endless progression of rooms all around the king.[21]

There is nothing particularly innovative about the architecture of Versailles. The rules of French classical architecture were set by Claude Perrault when he redesigned the east front of the palace of the Louvre in Paris in 1667: The *piano nobile* was defined by a tall porch of stone columns sitting on a rusticated

·99·

base and anchored on each side by slightly protruding pavilions. A strong cornice and deeply cut lintels etched the composition into the stone, while Perrault designed the windows in a rhythm of arches and pediments. This design became a formula, a way of summing up the ideals of proportion of which architects from Vitruvius to Alberti had spoken and turning them into a kind of architectural wallpaper that could serve as the front for a bank, a palace, a home, or even a church. Architects delighted in their ability to stretch these formulas by incorporating different forms of ornament or stone or containing disparate programs, but the basic recipe was the same. An important building should look the same, no matter what it really was or where it stood.[22]

**Figure 5.17: Louis Le Vau,
Château of Vaux-le-Vicomte,
begun 1657**

Versailles was just the most important of all of them, and the largest. It became the model for palaces all over Western Europe. Its forecourt, its grand staircase, its chapel, its garden terraces, and its basic layout were repeated in smaller versions from St. Petersburg to Madrid. What is remarkable about this architecture is how clearly it represents the reign of a visual, male, idealized structure of power.

First these structures were both centralized and uniform. They all revolved around a central axis. You would walk in through the front door, marked by a pedimented porch, and the exterior line on which you entered would continue all the way through the building to the most important space of the building, usually up a flight of stairs and in the rear. Another axis would cross this progression at right angles and lead you to the secondary spaces. At Versailles the designers didn't quite get this right because the building was constructed

Figure 5.18: André Le Nôtre, Louis Le Vau, Gardens, Château of Vaux-le-Vicomte, 1661

over a few generations, but most buildings based on this model will take you straight to the throne room, court of justice, chapel, or central hall. Along the way they will offer you a chance to go off to the programs that support this function, such as the cabinets of the minister or a dining room. The basic formula works for houses as well as for grand buildings. In some ways our stately homes are still based on this principle. The entry hall is a place that is still a plain, almost exterior space of stone and columns. A central axis leads to the living room and a view of a landscape controlled by man beyond. A crossing line takes you off to the more intimate rooms for dining or study.

Figure 5.19: Louis Le Vau, Château of Versailles, 1688

The facade represents these spaces but also represses them in favor of the idea of order in general: The repetitive march of columns and windows stands for a general sense of rhythm, of everything's being in its place, that contains even the central statement of the building. The building is a composition on its own. The most important, formal facade faces the city or whatever the avenue of approach might be. The garden facade becomes slightly more animated, as if the building were spilling out into and becoming part of domesticated nature. The side facades exist only to support these two faces and to strengthen the independence of the overall construction. The building can keep spreading out endlessly, as Versailles (or Mount Vernon) seems to do, as long as the architecture supports these central principles, often by making the central pavilion taller and more richly ornamented.

Figure 5.20: François Mansart, Château of Maisons, 1646 (engraving by Perelle)

These principles might seem simple, but they had far-reaching effects. By coming together into such a clearly ordered facade and such an autonomous building, they reinforced and finally realized the age-old architectural ideal of creating a small piece of perfection that stood in contrast with the real complexities of the world around it. By subjugating the interior to the two axes and filling out the spaces in between with whatever rooms might be needed to make the house or palace work, the architecture gave an absolute importance to the space of appearance over the activities of everyday life. By creating a world of stone, columns, pediments, and string courses, this architecture imprisoned itself in a strict, completely academic way of making spaces and objects. By surrounding smaller spaces with larger forms, and detaching those forms from the surrounding scene, this architecture created a world unto itself that needed a vast amount of financial and natural resources to support it. The ideal was built, and it was a monumentally expensive one.

The details of the interior, meanwhile, flowed from this overall pattern. In the next chapter I will discuss the perversion, deformation, and final liberation of some of the spaces of the interior. The main state rooms of such palaces as the one at Versailles, however, were designed as continuations of the themes of the exterior. They were taller than was necessary, opened up to one another because they all had to exist on the ceremonial axes, and were decorated with furnishings that specified the messages of the architecture. At Versailles the main salons were painted to represent the conquests of Louis XIV and mythological representations of his power. The chests, tables, and chairs were miniature versions of the architecture, carried out in woods that were as hard (and precious) as stone. At no place could you ever ascertain the way things were actually constructed or out of what they had been made. The stone completely covered the rubble that was used to make the insides of the walls, the ceilings and floors covered the wood beams, and the wood itself was polished to mirrored perfection. Where there were empty spaces, they were painted or hung with tapestries that brought other worlds into the interior. Nothing here was real; nothing here could be known about the real relationship of things. All was appearance; all was order; all was the power to construct a complete world into which you could fit only yourself.

That world continued out into the gardens, which emptied space of trees, of natural features, and of anything that might form a barrier to the eye. Then the garden designers erected mazes, shaded walks, and little bosquets within these terraces. Thus they created separate little interiors or specific rituals, whether of the highly regulated plays of courtship or of the outdoor plays that continued to instruct the court on morals. As the architectural historian Manfredo Tafuri has pointed out, these gardens became the models for urban design. To the architects of French classicism, the city was like an untamed wood, waiting to be cut open and controlled by axes.[23]

Just as Pope Alexander VII had connected the Campidoglio, the Piazza d'Italia, and the square of St. Peter's, so the kings of France cut Paris open with a line that ran from the center (or near center) of the Louvre all the way to what was to become the Place de l'Étoile, leaving extensive gardens in its wake. They cut further boulevards along the main routes out to the far corners of the realm and ended them at toll booths, designed by the architect Claude-Nicolas Ledoux, that controlled and taxed all goods coming into the city. The most concise embodiment of this desire to treat the city and the whole space of the country as an unformed wilderness that could be subjected to central power is a small plaque in the ground in the plaza Puerta del Sol in Madrid. It is the ground zero from which all distances in Spain are measured, the point from which the space of the whole country makes sense.

Figure 5.21: Louis-Robert Heyrault, *Les Chevaux de Marly*, 1859

By the late seventeenth century architects had boiled all this down to a system. The architecture became simpler, sparser, larger, and more repetitive. The École des Beaux-Arts—the central state school of architecture—developed a

· *103* ·

method of teaching that codified the rules described above and inculcated them into a select group of young men who would then go out and design the central institutions of the state. It was a system that worked for more than two centuries, reaching its apogee under the realm of Napoleon III in the third quarter of the nineteenth century, when young architects from all around the world, including the future leading architects of the United States, came to study there, and the emperor relied on the teachings of the École to create a completely rationalized Paris where there was no place for revolution. At another scale, the architect Jean-Nicolas-Louis Durand created a book that showed how starting from a simple geometric figure such as a square, and using the full panoply of classical architecture, you could create infinitely complex and varied buildings, that all would still look alike since they were created from the same building blocks. Straight from the mind of the designer, through the control of the trained eye and the power of the state, came a world of clear, concise, independent forms and spaces, an order realized.[24]

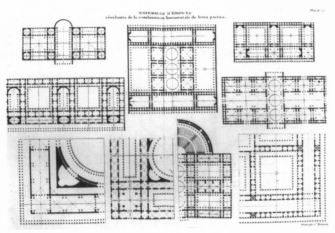

**Figure 5.22: Jean-Nicolas-Louis Durand,
Ensembles d'Édifices, from his *Précis*, 1802**

In 1778 Ledoux designed a small city in the east of France that summed up these principles. Arc-et-Senans was set up as a royal saltworks. In it the salt that came out of the mineral springs of the area was refined, thus enriching the royal coffers. Ledoux designed the complex as a perfect circle, so that we can see it as a *mandala* for the realm. From it roads radiated back into the country and out into the forest, where they became the hunting allées that the king used to mine the forest for his game. The ring was formed by stone buildings that contained dormitories and processing spaces. In the center stood the house of the director of the works, who was meant to hold forth at the end of a long set of steps. He also lived in the rigidly symmetrical world of the cubical house. On each side stood the storehouses in which the salt was kept. All around the house was the productive emptiness of a yard.

Arc-et-Senans is famous for its "speaking" ornament, stone that was cut to look like blocks of salt or like water spilling forth from the earth. The buildings themselves made it clear what went on in this complex, who was in control, and how the system of production, the system of architecture, and the people who filled out those systems all fitted together. There is a sparse and elegant beauty to the place, one that sums up the dreams of a world in which the world and its riches can be transformed into proportioned spaces of production.[25]

Figure 5.23: Claude-Nicolas Ledoux, Saltworks at Chaux, 1778

Ledoux and his fellow visionary Étienne-Louis Boullée dreamed of even grander structures. Boullée proposed a cenotaph for Newton that was a perfect globe on an immense scale. On the outside it would be a white object sitting in the landscape. On the inside the space would be dark, immense, and completely spherical, rotating around a model of Newton's universe and lit by holes that aligned with the constellations. Day for night, heaven on earth, the real disappearing into its abstract laws: This was an architecture carried about as far as it could go. Boullée specified his visions into such institutions as a proposed national library in which the central axis became the one and only space, with the book stacked up in terraced tiers around it and covered with a seemingly endless vault. He also wanted to build a national museum that was all columns and empty space, in which people and art disappeared into "an architecture of shadows."[26]

Two projects by Ledoux sum up this unreal architecture. The first is his 1784 theater at Besançon. This was a place where the three scenes could be enacted in an architecture that was sparse and refined enough to swallow up all meanings and imperfections. The building was a cube surmounted by a pyramid and containing a semicircle; the space of spectacle was reduced to a play of geometric blocks. Ledoux did a remarkable drawing of this space, in which the theater appears in the pupil of a giant eye. The gaze of a god, the architect, or the grand creator of a world encompassed its creation in the blink of an eye.

Figure 5.24: Étienne-Louis Boullée, *Cenotaph for Sir Isaac Newton*, 1784

Figure 5.25: Claude-Nicolas Ledoux, *Interior View*, Theater at Besançon, 1784

On the eve of the French Revolution Ledoux proposed an ideal city. In it all systems of production, all forms of living, all rituals of everyday life would have their own forms. Square, rectangular, and circular buildings would house everyone and everything. One of those buildings, the most expressive in its form, was the *oikèma*. This was the place where young men would gather when they were ready to become adult citizens. Their rite of passage was to lose their virginity to specially trained young maidens. The whole building was shaped like a penis, its central axis culminating in the chamber of manhood, its spaces filled out with chambers of pleasure. Here Ledoux brought the erection of a grand order back to its social basis: the assertion of male power over women, the world, and themselves.[27]

For all its abstraction, grandeur, and beauty, the idealizing architecture created in the Italian Renaissance and perfected in France in the eighteenth century came down to this building: a stone penis, sitting as a solitary form in the landscape. What is especially perverse is that you would never be able to perceive the penis as such; it was a form that appeared only in plan. Cesariano may have presented man impregnating the roundness of the world with an orthogonal order through the power of his erection, but by the time Ledoux worked this idea out into a building, it had become so subsumed into the process of designing and building that it had become invisible.

Classical architecture turned male power into a system that was so elaborate, so codified, and so absolute that it could bury any connection to sexual and social power plays. Architects created forms that realized a state power ever more divorced from real human beings, whether men or women. Only in the notations the architects make for themselves—namely, plans—can you read the true nature of what they are doing. The male architect himself becomes a god, looking down on the world in a plan or in a central perspective, subjecting everything to his idealizing tendencies, and remaking the world in his own image. Meanwhile, that image has dissolved into the grids and lines that he once thought his erection created.

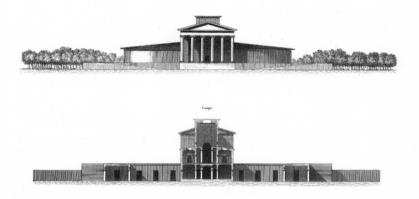

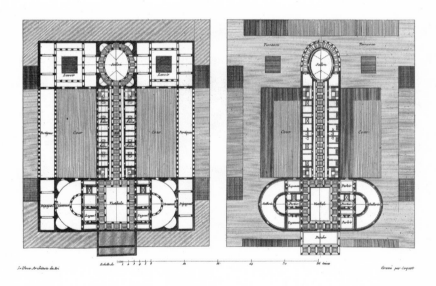

Figure 5.26: Claude-Nicolas Ledoux, *Oikèma*, 1790

THE GILDED CAGE

IN 1660 THE DUTCH PAINTER EMANUEL DE WITTE, whom we know today more for his church interiors than for his domestic scenes, produced *Interior with a Woman Playing the Virginals*. De Witte took great care to render the place and the activity of the title. In the foreground a woman sits with her back to the viewer, playing the instrument. A mirror reflects her face, but she turns away, toward anonymity. Her chair is made out of rectangular elements that the painter has placed on a stone checkerboard square that in turn puts everything in its place. Square patches of light form a counterpoint to the geometries of furniture and floor that you can imagine is still further complicated by the notes the woman is playing. Point and counterpoint, multiple layers of order, systems of proportion that slide by one another: Here a world much more slippery than the grand facades of architecture opens up.

That world gains depth as you look further into the painting. The woman is not alone. In the bed on the other side of the central doorway, you can just make out the shape of a sleeping man. Judged from the clothes piled up on a nearby chair, he is a soldier. Through the door you can glimpse a whole other world. A succession of rooms leads finally to a window through which you can see a glimpse of a tree-shaded yard. There a maid is sweeping the ground.[1]

Much is shown in great detail in this painting, but even more is implied. The relationship between the man and the woman, the music she is playing, her personality, the world outside, the shape of the house in which all this is taking place—all these elements are present, can be deduced, or can be assumed, but none of them is spelled out. This is not a window into a perfect world but a glimpse into a world of dreams, shadows, objects, and desires, all framed in such a way that you are never quite sure where things begin and end. You can drift endlessly through the rooms, past the objects, and around the implications of this painting without ever truly knowing the story. Instead you get a fragment. You see a reflection of momentary relationships, of the beauty of how things appear for a moment, that is pregnant with the poignancy of the past and the promised feats of the future.

Figure 6.1: Emanuel de Witte, *Woman Playing the Virginals*, 1660

This is a relatively humble—though by no means working-class—world. There are no columns, no central axes, no facades. This is a protected world, where the outside comes inside only in bits and pieces. The light that enters from the side, the map that you can barely see in the second room, and the furnishings themselves all are imported, placed, ordered, cleaned, and made part of a scenery of daily life. It is a place of maps, mirrors, and paintings, of lushly descriptive surfaces that tell you about other worlds, or the world around you, without idealizing them or claiming they are something other than what you can see with your eye. It is a world based on observation, deduction, logic, and reverie, not on stories, a single point, or preexisting rules. It is a world in which the relationship between you and the objects and people around you is continually in question.

It is also a world of women. The man is invisible, his presence only implied. It is a world not of great deeds and morals but of sex, of music, of cleaning. It is a world where the woman keeps house according to her taste and dictates. It is the interior that is the woman's space.

Emanuel de Witte's world was one that appeared in the Low Countries of the Rhine Delta at the end of the sixteenth century. For various historical reasons Holland escaped many of the social tendencies that created the rigid prisons of classical form in which men and women found themselves caught in more southern climes. Perhaps this was because Holland had to create itself out of sea and swamp and thus had a tradition of cooperative water stewardship that proved more durable than any aristocratic or royal occupation. Perhaps it was also the result of the fact that the country came to wealth and power not just on the basis of the rich agricultural land it wrested from the North Sea but mainly as a trading nation that opened itself up to foreigners and their goods and judged the world only according to its concrete trading and use value. The Dutch invented the stock exchange and many of the systems of financial management still in use today, and out of this economy they built a society in which common sense, pragmatism, and the ability to ascertain the physical value of an object reigned supreme.[2]

Thus there was little need in Holland for either the layers of aristocracy and morality or the deep division between the sexes common in Italy and France. This is not to say that there was no aristocracy and that women were the equal of men. There was a deep gap between rich and poor, and only a few families held power. Women were barred from many professions and from much legal power, though they did practice activities such as painting much more freely than in other countries. Moreover, the smallness of the country and its dense urban concentrations created environments in which there was little room for grand facades, great axes, and vast open spaces. Every part of the land that could be used or inhabited was. Thus the country emerged as a collage of carefully tended, meticulously crafted, and assiduously maintained fragments of order.

The Dutch developed a way of thinking about and representing this world that differed radically from the single-point perspective grid of the Albertian window. As Svetlana Alpers has pointed out, for the Dutch the model of a painting was a mirror, not a window. In it they hoped to bring together all the objects around them, fix them in perspective, and represent them so that the idea lay not in their own perfection but in the fact that one should not be able to tell the real thing apart from its representation. She points out that a confluence of art and science created a particular kind of space in seventeenth-century Dutch art. The discoveries of Antonie van Leeuwenhoek, the inventor of the microscope who was also the executor of Vermeer's estate, and Johannes Kepler broadened the visible world. The work of map makers, whose skills were necessary adjuncts to trade, fixed the boundaries and contours of that world ever more clearly. The work of irrigation specialists, town planners, and even such pioneer firemen as Jan van der Heyden, who was also the most financially successful painter of Europe, brought that world under ever more precise control.[3] The painter, mirror maker, and map maker all performed a similar function within this emerging man-made world (the Dutch invented the word "landscape," or "made land"): They framed, reflected, and fixed that world so that it could be known.[4] There was no other world here than that which was continually remade by man through observation and craft.

·III·

The result was a reality woven together out of objects, appearances, reflections, and structures, all caught in moments at which they make sense and maintained in that state by craft. That craft was not just one of making objects or trading deals but one of cleaning, arranging, and playing alive the hidden orders of music. The tasks of the woman in the home were part of an overall order, rather than what was necessary to maintain the men's order. Women were not circles to be impregnated by male squares. Both men and women were objects caught in the same shifting grids of a perspective that was, significantly enough, defined by two points at either point of the frame rather than by a single point at the end of a long axis.[5]

Figure 6.2: Pieter de Hooch, *Woman Preparing Vegetables*, 1657

Moreover, in Dutch art the woman finally appears. In the work of painters such as Pieter de Hooch, Gabriel Metsu, Gerard Ter Borch, and, of course, Jan Vermeer, she appears not as the Mother Mary, as a redeemed whore, as a sainted martyr, or as a demure courtesan, but as a housewife at work or in love. She cleans, she picks lice out of her children's hair, she pours milk, she reads letters, and she marvels at the beauty of a pearl. She is at home, in her element, and there is a beauty to that world. If the man appears, he is an intruder, a merrymaker, a seducer, or a gentleman calling, not the primary focus of the painting.

In these paintings the inside world is enough. In many of Vermeer's great images the exterior does not even appear. It is screened out by shutters, kept behind doors, and otherwise removed from our view. In *The Good Housewife* by de Hooch, the canal you can see through the open doorway appears to be no more than an extension of the house, just another interior in which everything is in its place.

Figure 6.3: Pieter de Hooch,
The Good Housewife, **1663**

These interiors were in reality as plain and as utilitarian as interiors had always been. The walls were covered in white plaster, the ceilings were made of wood beams, and the rooms' simple shapes allowed for a variety of different functions to take place. In that sense they were no different from the multipurpose rooms of the Middle Ages. The floors had become more lavish and were often made out of intricate arrangements of tile or stone. The chests and storage spaces became grander, to keep in scale with the room itself. Objects of use proliferated, so that kitchen utensils, clothes, lamps, and clocks were everywhere. What strikes us most of all in the painted scenes of these interiors is the pervasive presence of maps, mirrors, and paintings. Foreign observers were astonished by the presence of these objects in even the most humble homes. The Dutch had brought the whole world under their control by domesticating it.[6]

To the women in these interiors this process was still largely a one-way street. They read at windows by the soft light that spilled over the shutters, rather than write of their own exploits and explorations. They played music written by others. They looked in the mirror and saw themselves, or they looked at maps and saw places they would never see. For them the world was an artificial and artifactual place. The maps, mirrors, and paintings stood in for the real thing and allowed the women to know them in terms of their abstract internal relationships. In a famous painting by Vermeer now hanging in the Metropolitan Museum, the woman can only dream. All around her and behind her the house creates spaces that are confined, a labyrinth of chairs and desks and walls that hem her into a constricted space. The eye looks for ways out but always keeps circling back to the woman, whose eyes are closed as she dreams of another world.

It is amazing how defined the space of human beings is in these paintings. The figures in Vermeer's paintings are fixed behind tables, in chairs, framed by maps behind them, placed on gridded floors, and finally framed by the architecture and art of the interior. This is a self-sufficient world, where everything can be brought in but from which there does not appear to be any means of escape. The woman admiring the strand of pearls can only gaze in admiration at the crafted object of beauty, her mouth open in amazement, her head turned toward the light, her wealth spread out in front of her. There is no place to go other than inward, toward the gaze that connects the object to the self and dissolves them into a crafted moment of beauty.

Figure 6.4: Jan Vermeer,
Young Woman Reading a Letter, 1657

This is certainly the world not only of the domestic interior but also of the personal interior. Nothing is said or done; all is only implied or dreamed about. Objects become symbols, like slippers by the bed or dogs that represent faithfulness. The woman turns her head away from the painter and the viewer. She turns inward, creating her own world both around her and within herself.

The interior collects and arranges the material fruits of the labors of discovery, agriculture, craft, and trade. The soul then drinks it all in, and the body goes about its work of maintaining domestic order. Domesticity is another order than any of the ones implied in Serlio's scenes. It is not a place of meaning, of understanding, of deeds, or of warfare and defense. It is a place dedicated to continually re-creating, representing, and maintaining itself. It is a place of work, and the main work is to keep itself in a state that will allow for more work.

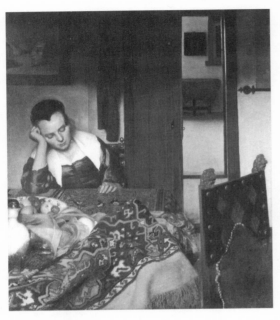

Figure 6.5: Jan Vermeer, *Girl Asleep*, 1650

The qualities of its spaces are both more open and more contained. In the Dutch city there are few monumental objects and even fewer grand axes that predate the nineteenth century. There is no high point, no expansive gardens, no symmetry laid over complexity. Walk along the canals of Amsterdam, and you will find yourself continually turning along radial canals that lead nowhere. The middle of the street is not an empty place of appearance, but a working place, a heterotopia where you can only float and see the world around you reflected. The facades themselves are endless variations on the same theme of large windows that let as much light into the interior as possible, with little focus or concentration on any central point. Even the door is usually to one side or the other.

Space here flows, reflects, and slips between the cracks of bricks and buildings, never completing itself, always leading back to itself, and spiraling inward toward the protected insides of buildings. There all the orders of the outside world layer themselves into objects of use and representation but never resolve themselves into one particular place of importance. Space shifts as you use it, move through it, remake it, represent it. Space flows exactly because everything is so defined. You must place yourself continually in this world, weave it together by your daily, normal, forgettable actions. Beauty is in the eye of the beholder, a seer who is also a maker and a knower.

The Dutch thus opened up a space for the woman. It was a space of flows through orders, a place of making, a place of representation, a place that moved inward rather than outward, a space that created relationships between the self and others through things in use and seen. The Dutch domestic interior became the model for a space women could open up for themselves everywhere, though it appears in different forms in other cultures.

To the English, the space of Dutch domesticity was both familiar and imported during the realm of the Dutch king William and his English mate, Mary. The vogue for interiors, for gardens that were made up of precise pieces rather than grand terraces, and the interest in the art of representation swept the aristocracy. It met up with a long tradition of palaces and places of representation that were considerably more *ad hoc* and rambling in their appearance than their French counterparts. Both traditions were, however, soon swept away by the importation of exactly such traditions by the Restoration monarchy, the German princes, and such architects as Lord Burlington, Inigo Jones, Nicholas Hawksmoor, and even the Fleming John Vanbrugh, who imitated Versailles and the palaces of Italy in the country homes and government buildings they designed for the English aristocracy. It is interesting to note that only in such colonies as those on the eastern seaboard of America do some of the humble, *ad hoc* and inward-turned qualities of Dutch spaces appear— whether because of the reduced circumstances of the habitations there or because of the Dutch influence in the settlements on the Hudson—and thus become building blocks for the colonial revival of the nineteenth century.

In France the turn inward occurred under the reign of Louis XIV himself. After he had come home from his wars, after he had commissioned the palace at Versailles, and after he had tired of the formality of his life, he began to create an alternate world for himself and his mistresses. This was a world of sensuality, a world that was lived in small cabinets or rooms, rather than in the grand spaces of formal appearance, and a world in which women played an increasingly large role. The château at Marly-le-Roi, which he commissioned for his mistress Madame de Montespan to serve as a royal trysting place, sported rooms that were small, relatively low, and disconnected from the axes that controlled the overall building. Here the king did away with ceremony and indulged in the joys of dalliance and conversation.[7] But even at a formal scale things started to fall apart—or at least into another kind of place. The Galerie des Glaces, or Hall of Mirrors, finished in 1686, was an immense

Figure 6.6: J. H. Mansart and Charles le
Brun, Galerie des Glaces, Château of
Versailles, 1686

space, but one that had no clearly defined center other than the one implied
by the central axis of the garden that you could see from its windows. The
use of mirrors on the walls facing those windows doubled the appearance
of the outside, and made all the inhabitants in the space actors watching
themselves perform. The rigid places and rituals started to twirl around
one another.[8]

Such was certainly true in the furnishings that started to eat away at the grand
architectural orders at the end of the seventeenth century. The rococo or Style
Louis XV did away with rigid symmetry and sometimes even with the strict
definition of separate objects and planes. One observer described the result:

> The individual members, the profiling are handled with the most extreme
> subtlety. The old classical rules seem forgotten. The profiles are doubled
> and tripled, as well as overspread at pleasure with an ever changing
> dynamic ornament, that enlivens with dazzling lights and deep shadows
> surfaces already curved in themselves. Fluttering banderoles, draperies,
> and garlands of stucco overspread otherwise vacant surfaces, unite abut-
> ting elements. Figures, shellwork, cartouches and masks hide the points
> of intersection. Every hard even line is consciously avoided. A veritable
> vibration is achieved. Round arches rise against gable-segments, only to

be immediately interrupted by a projection. The cartouches and shields turn and bend, curved lines predominate. Nowhere does one encounter a uniform circle or square, for its place has been taken by the more exciting forms, suggesting movement and depth, of the oval and rectangle.[9]

The deformation of classical objects and their merger into interlacing forms tended to create a sense of unity in these rooms that came more from their spatial characteristics than it did from the themes that had given their names to such Versailles moments of royal propaganda as the Salon of Venus, the Salon of Mars, or the Salon of Diana. Now there was the Oeil de Boeuf, or Bull's-Eye Room, named after the window of that shape that cut through the cornice line and rose into the coved ceiling, spreading waves of light and ornament all around it.

Figure 6.7: Pierre Le Pautre, Antichambre de l'Oeil de Boeuf, Château of Versailles, 1701

The rococo did not just create a unified and continuous surface; it also shattered the separation between a structural or compositional order that contained decoration, furniture, or painted messages. Instead the answering curves of chairs, moldings, and paintings by such artists as Watteau covered all surfaces, subjugating the discipline of columns to the crescendo of curves. Ornament, the handmaiden of architecture, was smothering the elements of representation in her sensuous embrace.

You can find the true flowering of the rococo not in the grand state apartments of the Louvre but in the private hotels or town houses of Paris. The Salon de la Princesse in the Hôtel de Soubise, designed in 1739 by Germain Boffrand, is an oval room dedicated to Eros and Psyche—their story is told in paintings that spread out between the arches and curves of the door surrounds—but mainly memorable for continuous movement. The curve of the room is picked up in the rise and fall of the arches over doors and windows that in turn replicate themselves over the blank panels in between these real and virtual openings. The curves unite in the undulating line of the ceiling, which is treated like a pale blue cloud tethered to the fantastical dance of the room by gilt waves and curlicues. Putti float on all this movement, and a crystal chandelier ties the whole space together into a circle of light. There is no hierarchy in this space; there is only the continual dissolution of the framing arches into the overlapping stretches of the decoration itself. All is color; all is movement; all is light.

Figure 6.8: Germain Boffrand, Salon de la Princesse, Hôtel de Soubise, Paris, 1739

Figure 6.9: François Boucher,
Venus at Vulcan's Forge, 1732

The scale of these spaces is both more intimate and more indeterminate. In the paintings of Watteau or Boucher a prototypical space appears: "[A]rabesque elements unite the real and the unreal of central field and outer border. . . . The last echoes of the baroque massiveness disappear in evanescent incorporeality."[10] Men and women clad in diaphanous clothes engage in the pursuit of pleasure on islands where the real world remains far away, where nature is nothing but soft textures, and where the sun is always rising or setting. This dreamworld continues into the salons around the paintings, where the structure of the building and the real activities that take place within them are replaced with an elaborate play of lines and rituals. The culture of etiquette that blossomed in the eighteenth century was perhaps made most famous by *Les Liaisons Dangereuses*, which translated all political and personal actions into carefully turned phrases, gestures, and dances of innuendo.[11] The architecture of the spaces in which such intrigues took place realized this culture of conceit and deceit. The rococo is the first self-conscious style, the first system of designing the pieces of the interior based not on a working method or belief in the purpose of the building but on the desire to make the whole appear as something that it was not (at least according to our tendency to conflate the real with the structural): something unreal; something flowing; something that would unite bodies, forms, and gestures into a continuous dance of ephemeral surfaces.

Figure 6.10: François de
Cuvilliés, Spiegelsaal,
Amalienburg, Munich, 1739

To achieve these aims, the artists of the rococo turned away from classical sources and toward nature for their inspiration. Instead of columns and friezes, they decorated their rooms with interpretations of waves, boughs, flowers, trees, rocks, and clouds. When they did use quasi-structural elements such as columns, their connective elements, like bases or capitals, would drip and merge into their surroundings. The artists of the rococo showed little respect for the correct handling of masses, preferring the logic of the eye as it wandered through the whole space. They did not try to create ordered interiors that would stand in stark contrast with the unformed nature or urban environment outside, but rather tried to re-create nature within the interior itself, thus eliding the borders between the real and the unreal. At its most extreme, which you could find in the German palaces created by the French designer François de Cuvilliés, such as the Amalienburg in Munich (1734–39), you would be hard pressed to locate a real space, a place that would define you in a particular hierarchy. All was flow; all was style; all was a myth of dissolution.

There is a logic to such rooms, of course. It is a logic that comes from the need to create a real, inhabitable world after the parameters for the new world have been set. The rooms of the eighteenth century were places that filled out the grand orders established by the nascent state and used the wealth that had been conquered and rationalized by that same mechanism. Once the rules had been set, they could not exist as empty abstractions. Warfare and rationalization could not be lived experience. Thus those in control of the world needed a place where they could connect the dots, the columns, and the objects they had gained and weave out of them a tapestry that would give meaning to their achievements. From the work of conquest and the belief in enlightenment, they turned toward the delight of appearances and the logic of style. The cycles of fashion and the flows of words, fabrics, or rooms did not so much contradict the classical orders as fill them out.[12] Women had the function of being the content, the prize, and the medium by which men could act, and the lavish interiors of the early eighteenth century became their place.

It is important to realize how circumscribed this world was, both by the amount of money it took to create it and by the fact that such a place could exist only inside the heavily guarded precincts of the male palaces. The very success of the rococo rooms made men wary. They saw the new interior as taken over completely by style. Male critics of the style identified it as a feminine development. We still identify the rise of the rococo with the power of the king's mistresses, with the turn of French culture inward from conquest toward the elaboration of its internal rituals and rules, and with the rising importance of fashion as it was defined by the clothes worn by the women at court.

Men in both France and England blamed women for the embellishment of the basic rules of language and architecture with all the decorative flourishes that, to these conservative critics, seemed to suffocate those very rules. Scholars and pundits alike criticized women for not being seriously interested in the underlying meaning of words, gestures, or building; they cared only about the appearance, the decoration, and the superfluous ornamentation. If women made the world of fashion and elegant appearance their own, then it could not be a world that had any intrinsic meaning. Nothing mattered in the world of fashion, and therefore, it should be contained and controlled by a world in which things did matter.[13]

The world that wealthy women fashioned for themselves did become a center of power and attention. In 1600 the Italian Catherine de Vivonne married the French Marquis de Rambouillet. She moved to Paris and turned her private reception quarters into the location of a regular gathering of the most important artists, writers, philosophers, and politicians of the era. What was said in her salon became the standard of taste and culture.

There was nothing particularly exceptional about the design of these spaces, though Madame de Rambouillet's *Chambre Bleue* was famous for its sophistication. They were decorated in the style of the period and not particularly exuberant. Instead they were typical. The way in which this rather intimate room, whose walls were painted and hung with silk, was furnished promoted conversation rather than rituals. Furniture was by now light enough that it could be easily moved. Morsels of food rather than elaborate meals were served on small tables, and the chairs were padded and low, so that men could recline in them and women could find room for all their clothes. Paintings of such salons show small groupings of people, their heads turned toward one another, their clothes flowing around them. The scene is punctuated by beautifully made serving pieces, a few books, and the carefully crafted elements of the furniture. The architecture of these settings disappears into the dark background, its stark forms dissolving into the chiaroscuro at the edge of the frame.[14]

It was in such salons that more and more important decisions were made. Instead of rigid degrees and hierarchies of appearance, it was the wit of repartee that determined policy. The kings and noblemen themselves preferred these kinds of intimate and warm surroundings to the coldness of the palaces. Versailles was still nominally the center of the universe, but more and more the state was run through the intrigues and fashions of the salons. This was true not only in France. All over Europe men retreated into the small cabinets, round salons, curving spaces, and comfortable furnishings where women set the tone. You could even see the American Revolution as a revolt of the study and the salon against the imposed grandeur of the governor's palace.

Figure 6.11 François Boucher, *Madame de Pompadour*, 1758

Nor was this a phenomenon restricted to the upper classes. As Europe became more wealthy, and as the growth in consumption created a nascent middle class, the undifferentiated spaces of the city began to separate into more and more specialized rooms. By the eighteenth century the parlor or salon had become an essential part of most urban houses and apartments, even if it was not a part of the hovels of the poor. In these spaces the woman worked and appeared. It was here that she sewed; it was here that she received guests. Even if her chances for going out into the world were restricted, she could bring the world into her own space. Furniture, hangings, and knickknacks proliferated, each more specialized and more artfully arranged than the one before. To Alexander Pope, it was a world with great pretensions:

> And now, unveil'd, the Toilet stands display'd.
> Each Silver Vase in mystic Order laid.
> First, rob'd in White, the Nymph intent adores
> With Head uncover'd, the cosmetic Pow'rs.
> A heav'nly Image in the Glass appears,
> To that she bends, to that her Eyes she rears;
> Th' inferior Priestess, at her Altar's side,
> Trembling, begins the sacred Rites of Pride.
> Unnumber'd Treasures ope at once, and here
> The various Off'rings of the World appear;
> From each she nicely culls with curious Toil,
> And decks the Goddess with the glitt'ring Spoil.
> This Casket India's glowing Gems unlocks,
> And all Arabia breathes from yonder Box.
> The Tortoise here and Elephant unite,
> Transform'd to Combs, the speckled and the White. . . .[15]

Figure 6.12: Aubrey Beardsley, *The Toilet*, from *The Rape of the Lock*, 1896

The world of women that Pope portrayed in *The Rape of the Lock* was one in which meaning got lost in irony, and the trivial turned, even in the title itself, around the meaningful. It was a world made up only of gestures, dreams, and innuendoes. The only actions were those performed by men (the "rape"). The magical world that women had woven for themselves for centuries now finally had the means at its disposal to create a counter to the world outside. The woman could defeat the rape. It was a counter that mimicked the usefulness of all objects out there, the warfare and the ritual, but did it in a reflexive manner: The woman looked into the mirror and re-created the world all around her, instead of conquering new worlds or hoping to create any change. She reacted and re-created, delighting in the sensuous beauty of it all.

Figure 6.13: Richard Mique, Boudoir of Marie-Antoinette, Château of Fontainebleau, 1785

Yet already under Louis XV the reaction had set in. The Petit Trianon, itself a retreat from the formal splendors of the court, was designed by Jacques-Ange Gabriel in 1762 in a style that consciously recalled the formal rigidity of Louis XIV, though in proportions and colors that were much lighter. Gabriel and such contemporaries as Claude Patte and even Claude-Nicolas Ledoux cleaned out the *rocaille* (the seashell decoration that was one of the mainstays of rococo decoration), the proliferation of branches and leaves, the melting curves, and the tapestry of interlocking arches in favor of empty planes. The Salon de la Reine in the Petit Trianon is small, intimate, and filled with low, broad furniture. It has a large mirror, set in an arch. But the arch here is broad and static, and it sits isolated between empty panels that are framed by thin gold bands. Where curls and curves appear, they are heraldic monograms. Only the rounded seat backs, the door pulls, and other elements where the body comes into contact with the architecture of the room are allowed to slide away from the rigidity of the formal scheme. There is a pronounced emphasis on thin, vertical, empty planes.

These interiors were more masculine in the way that French culture defined that term, but they were still comfortable and small-scaled. It was mainly male architects who sought to simplify and clean out the interior, but they could not deny the seductive comfort and sensuality of the rococo world. Instead they sought to discipline and contain that sensuality, tucking the fabric into straighter chairs, confining curves to places where the hand might move or the eye would see a connection between planes, and pairing the conversational excesses of the planes down to the *mot juste* of an architectural embellishment.

You can see the same development in England, where Robert and James Adam created cream-colored rooms with an icing of dotted, fretted, and floriated moldings defining paper-thin planes over the continuously white and gilt surfaces. In such houses as Osterley Park the structural elements of the architecture disappeared into light-colored planes, with ornament dancing all over the floors, ceilings, and walls. That ornament was not just abstract but often took the form of human figures in bas-relief, while fountains sprouted classical friezes. There was little logic here and no sense of articulating the structure that did the real "work" of holding up and dividing up the spaces. There was only a delight in the elements of order, thinned down to their merest essence and treated as just so much decoration.

Figure 6.14: Robert and James Adam, Etruscan Room, Osterley Park, 1761

The inspiration of the ornament was the rediscovery of the classical world. When Baron J. J. Winckelmann excavated Pompeii and Herculaneum in the 1750s, he brought to light the real statues and rooms that had existed only in hints in the surviving fragments and descriptions of the classical era. A craze for historical correctness swept Europe, with architects and artists clothing themselves in the mantle of scholarship and serious study. As such, neoclassicism was more than a style. It was an attempt to give to the field of architecture and interior decoration a serious foundation in an interpretation of texts and artifacts. The same École des Beaux-Arts that defined the social and economic role of the architect also defined the models he could use. Only if you were to engage in a serious study of classicism could you become

Figure 6.15: Jacques-Louis David, *Oath of the Horatii*, 1781

a good designer. This, of course, meant that amateurs and those who did not enter schools, such as the women who were barred from such halls of learning, would have little to say about the quality of the design. The spaces of the Enlightenment were meant to be correct, formal, male, and devoid of such issues of comfort.[16]

The space of the Enlightenment is the space of Jacques-Louis David. It is the space of *The Oath of the Horatii*, where men stand in the foreground, creating an interplay of lines that denote and constitute action, while the women are pushed off to the side, where they sit on simple furniture, curving and turning inward in mute grief. The architecture is sparse, rectilinear, and larger than life. It towers over and anchors the figures to an emptiness, a moral clarity that has no room for feelings, for textures, for surfaces, or for appearances.

The space of the French Revolution is the space of tennis courts, where citizens take public action, not the space of salons, where things happen without there being a clear reason or order to events. It is the space where everybody is equal, where the function of all things is clear, and where meaning is invented. It is the space of the workshops that appear in Diderot's *Encyclopédie,* blank rooms where machinery is taking over space.[17] In the space of light and reason, of violence and meaning, there is no room for the introspective, the delicate, the connective tissue of comfort, or the cycles of fashions.

And yet the Revolution itself became a style. It became a way of dressing, a way of speaking, and a way of decorating. The masters of this style were the decorators Charles Percier and Pierre-François-Léonard Fontaine. They performed the same function for Napoleon and his powerful wife Josephine that Le Brun had performed for Louis XIV. They gave shape to his vision of a new world that was completely rational and completely militarized. The palace at Compiègne became a place of brightly colored columns and heavy friezes. They shared with such designers as Thomas Hope in England and Thomas Jefferson in America an interest in creating highly formal enscenements of a revived classical world, in which one can imagine togas replacing breeches and Latin law and language replacing the subtleties of French or English.

Figure 6.16: Charles Percier and Pierre-François-Léonard Fontaine, Bedroom of the Empress Josephine, Château of Malmaison, 1812

At the heart of this vision of an absolutely refined classicism that subjected all activities to its rigid forms was something more ephemeral: the tent. Napoleon's empire was an artificial, temporary one, as were the archaeological re-creations of the noblemen and businessmen who hired Percier, Fontaine, and Hope. They were thin shells, collections of artifacts and statements of order, rather than heavy and structural embodiments of a fixed order. In 1803 Percier and Fontaine designed the empress's bedroom at Malmaison as a tent, complete with fabric and tent poles. This was a military tent, with swags and fasces reminding you of the conquering armies that might surround you if you stepped out of the fantasy. It was a tent nonetheless, a light and airy place that caused the architectural elements to disappear behind its folds.

Figure 6.17: Sir John Soane, Breakfast Room, Sir John Soane House, London, 1813

In 1812 the British architect Sir John Soane designed the breakfast parlor of his home at 13 Lincoln's Inn Fields in London as a space defined by a continually curved ceiling. Light entered the room from a lantern in the middle but also spilled around the sides of the ceiling, so that the ceiling seemed to float like a piece of fabric. The room was not defined by walls on all sides but flowed out into the adjacent passageways. Paintings, bookcases, and mirrors filled every available surface, so that the room became a collage of fragments of scholarship. The order of classicism dissolved into the thinnest, most ephemeral statement and then broke apart into the pieces out of which it was built.[18]

The days of grand male orders were over, at least on the inside. Men and women alike were building a new world for themselves. It was a place of comfort, conversation, domestic relationships, changing uses, and beautiful objects. Men continued to create more and more orders in the outside world, spreading their rational and warlike empire around the globe and opening up the cities of Western Europe to the unfaltering and harsh gaze of reason. Inside, a new world was emerging, a world where things were not that certain.

After the Revolution, David became the portraitist of Madame Récamier, who looks at us from her daybed. Her space is not one that is defined by architectural element. It is a flowing, undefined field of color, shade, and shadow. The woman turns toward us for inspection yet hides, like the housewife at the spinet in de Witte's painting, so that we cannot know what space she shelters in front of her. This is a new space, liberated from the confines of both ritual and fashion. It is a space that the woman can make for herself.

Figure 6.18: Jacques-Louis David, *Madame Récamier,* **1800**

7

THE DISCREET PLACES OF THE BOURGEOISIE

THEODORE DREISER'S 1900 NOVEL *SISTER CARRIE* traces the trajectory of a country girl as she enters the city. Drawn to Chicago by the promise of "making something of herself," she finds herself lost in a labyrinth, a place that is completely alien to her as a woman and a human being:

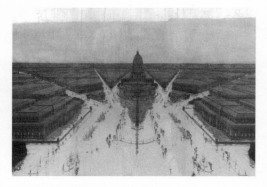

Figure 7.1: Daniel Burnham, *Civic Square,* from *Plan for Chicago,* 1908

Into this important commercial region the timid Carrie went. She walked east along Van Buren Street through a region of lessening importance, until it deteriorated into a mass of shanties and coal-yards, and finally verged upon the river. She walked bravely forward, led by an honest desire to find employment and delayed at every step by the interest of the unfolding scene, and a sense of helplessness amid so much evidence of power and force which she did not understand. These vast buildings, what were they? These strange energies and huge interests, for what purposes were they here? . . . when the yards of some huge stone corporation came into view, filled with spur tracks and flat cars, transpierced by docks from the river, and traversed overhead by immense trundling cranes of wood and steel, it lost all significance in her little world.[1]

She finds work in a factory, where she is hemmed in completely by the machinery of production. There is no place for her in the city, however exciting it might be. While she is lost in this world of aches and pains made real, the man who will seduce her, both "ruining" her and liberating her to become a woman of her own, is at home in the environment his wife has created.

A lovely home atmosphere is one of the flowers of the world, than which there is nothing more tender, nothing more delicate, nothing more calculated to make strong and just the natures cradled and nourished within it. Those who have never experienced such a beneficent influence will not understand wherefore the tear springs glistening to the eyelids at some strange breath of lovely music. The mystic chords which bind and thrill the heart of the nation, they will never know. Hurstwood's residence could scarcely be said to be infused with this home spirit. It lacked that toleration and regard without which the home is nothing. There was fine furniture, arranged as soothingly as the artistic perception of the occupants warranted. There were soft rugs, rich, upholstered chairs and divans, a grand piano, a marble carving of some unknown Venus by some unknown artist, and a number of small bronzes gathered from heaven knows where, but generally sold by the large furniture houses along with everything else which goes to make the "perfectly appointed house."[2]

In this comfortable and isolated world of the domestic suburban interior, the woman tries to create a place of culture and belonging for her philandering husband and her spoiled children by gathering all the myriad consumer goods the city has to offer. It is a holy place, a place where she creates a world of connections that seeks to weave its magic spell behind the forbidding facades of the metropolis. Carrie's great achievement is to create a facsimile of this, itself artificial, world. She can do that only because she is installed within it by her seducer, who rents an apartment for her:

> The rooms were comfortably enough furnished. There was a good Brussels carpet on the floor, rich in dull red and lemon shades, and representing large jardinieres filled with gorgeous, impossible flowers. There was a larger pier-glass mirror between the two windows. A large, soft, green, plush-covered couch occupied one corner, and several rocking chairs were set about. Some pictures, several rugs, a few small pieces of bric-a-brac, and the tale of contents is told. . . . The whole place was cozy, in that it was lighted by gas and heated by furnace registers. . . . By her industry and natural love of order, which now developed, the place maintained an air pleasing in the extreme.[3]

Figure 7.2: Clarence Cook, Frontispiece,
The House Beautiful, **1881**

Thus Carrie creates a place of order, a place where she can re-create herself as another person who is the very embodiment of the city. Her ability to buy into and re-create the realm to which women are assigned and through which they define themselves enables her to make her way in the city. By the end of the book she has become an actress, in complete control of her destiny in and through the city that is her stage.[4]

Carrie is the very embodiment of the middle-class woman who finally managed to create a powerful space for women in Western society but in so doing reaffirmed the prison of femininity men had created for her. Not every woman could do this. The nineteenth-century metropolis was the creation and playground of the middle class. It was a place of broad boulevards, parks, theaters, museums, cafés, shopping arcades, and train stations where, if you had the time and the money, you went to see, move, buy, and be seen. It was also a place of cramped rooms where every surface was covered with overlays of different patterns and where objects confronted you as you tried to find your way through this brave new world if you did not belong to either the land or the manor. It was the place where women ran the family, raised the children, and defined culture, while men built the city, made the rules, and bought the goods. Nineteenth-century middle-class space was the domain of Freud's ego and id and of the self-conscious identification of the male principle with control and the female principle with desire.

There was a profound emptiness at the heart of the crowded nineteenth-century city. It was an emptiness that came from both design and the logic of the separation between men and women and between classes. If you carried the most radical implications of the neoclassical movement all the way to its logical extreme, you wound up with the almost empty space of Boullée's cenotaph for Newton or David's *The Oath of the Horatii*, a place where all the attributes that you would associate with use, comfort, or even human scale disappeared, liberating a pure, empty space. This was the final achievement of the rationalizing conquest of the world: Power wore the mask of abstraction to such a degree that it was invisible.

This space was democratic and rational. Anyone who entered its noncommittal confines could manipulate it. As such it was the middle-class space supreme. The middle-class struggle for power and the march of industrialization through the landscape of Western Europe is a large story, but you can see it in its spaces. You can see it in the palaces of power that they converted into speculative apartment blocks, in the gridded business enterprises and mass-produced homes, and in the factories that had no particular meaning or message but purely and simply made space available.

Think about the new spaces of the nineteenth century, whether for work, living, or play. Instead of the hovels of the poor and the palaces of the rich, the one disappearing into the activities of everyday life and the other articulated for a particular client and purpose, there was the apartment. It was built up out of repetitive modules we would call rooms, produced in large quantities, and dependent on such hidden services as a concierge, water and sewage, and, later on, electricity and gas. Its rooms were designed for specific purposes but only in a generic sort of way. When you moved in, its walls were bare, the placement of outlets and service cores were predictable, and it disappeared into the repetitive facade of the street. It was as if the back rooms of Versailles had taken over, their bureaucratic extension of the plays of power carrying on without the centralizing control of the main pavilion.

Figure 7.3: Senate Square, Helsinki, 1813–51

The space of work was, of course, even more empty and denuded of specificity. The workroom of clerks who made up the core of the new middle class was an ever-extending bare room, a place where repetitive tasks took place in predictable spaces. Larger and larger expanses of low-ceilinged space were organized around their own central services, whether they were stairs or elevators or toilets or messenger services. Light and air were apportioned to each area in increasingly scientific manners. The factory was an empty space, as was the warehouse. There machines, their operation, and the storage of the goods they created took over space completely, and man became just an adjunct to the machinery.

Figure 7.4: John Wellborn Root, Interior of the
Phenix Buillding, Chicago, 1885

The spaces of gathering and movement were also
voids, though not in a negative sense. The ruling
classes still controlled the plazas of the new middle-class city, but spaces of leisure appeared: parks
and playgrounds, places for sports and assignation
and, most important, for shopping. Originally
these were spaces where anything could happen,
as long as it was controlled by the order of the
surrounding buildings or the laws of economics
and morals. They were not designed and had an
inherent danger to them: A woman could fall prey
there to the violence lurking below the surface of
the city or could find herself reduced to an unat-
tached state where she might wind up as a naked
playthng sitting between the fully clothed men of Manet's 1863 *Le Déjeuner
sur l'herbe*. In the empty space of the man-made city, the woman was no more
or less than an object to be seen, admired, or used.

Figure 7.5: Édouard Manet,
Le Déjeuner sur l'herbe, 1863

The greatest new spaces of movement, finally, were the sheds of train stations
and the boulevards. These were not quite completely inside or outside, since
they were both defined and open. The train shed was a glass canopy that
disappeared into the smoke of the trains or the glint of the sun. On the boulevards the continuous walls of the speculative apartment and office blocks
defined the mass of the city, the services defined the street, and only the
ceiling was missing. These so-called public open spaces were open at one end,
disappearing into the endless possibilities of future growth without being
grounded in a radiating center of power. They were merely fragments of the
future that was rebuilding the present through a predictable but open-ended
machinery of transformation. The future was limitless, the present uncertain.

This was an exciting but also a harsh and empty world, one in which writers
and artists of the nineteenth century felt a profound sense of loss and alienation. These were the streets where the shock of the new confronted people.
Here Dostoevsky's Raskolnikov finds the labyrinths of open-ended morality
that allows him both to commit his crime in the rented quarters of the pawn-
broker and to submit himself to the faceless punishment of a rational law.[1]

This is the place where Rousseau sees the evil of an impersonal world rising[6] and where Jefferson sees power rearing its ugly head.[7] This is the world where Marx and Engels can truly articulate their theory of alienation. For it is here that "all that is solid melts into air."[8] The gridded perspectival world of the Renaissance and the relentless conversion of all the natural world into reproducible fragments created a place that was no place and everywhere, where one had no clear relationship to the physical environment. This was the brave new modern world, the "maelstrom of modernity"[9] and the labyrinth of the city. Most of all, this was the world of William Blake:

Figure 7.6: Camille Pissarro, *Boulevard Montmartre, Winter Morning,* 1897

> I wander thro' each charter'd street,
> Near where the charter'd Thames does flow,
> And mark in every face I meet
> Marks of weakness, marks of woe.
>
> In every cry of every man,
> In every Infant's cry of fear,
> In every voice, in every ban,
> The mind-forg'd manacles I hear. . . .[10]

Figure 7.7: Factory, Plzen, Czechoslovakia

Man was imprisoned in a Frankenstein's monster of his own making, the city as monster and as living being. Ultimately the city and its machinery became one. At the end of the century Frank Lloyd Wright wrote one of the most stunning visions of such a world:

> Be gently lifted at nightfall to the top of a great downtown office building, and you may see how in the material image of man, at once his glory and menace, is this thing we call a city. There beneath, grown up in a night, is the monster leviathan, stretching acre upon acre into the far distance. High overhead hangs the stagnant pall of its fetid breath, reddened with the light from its myriad eyes endlessly everywhere blinking. Ten thousand acres of cellular tissue, layer upon layer, the city's flesh, outspreads enmeshed by intricate network of veins and arteries, radiating into the gloom, and there with muffled, persistent roar, pulses and circulates as the blood in your veins, the ceaseless beat of the activity to whose necessities it all conforms. Like to the sanitation of the human body is the drawing off of poi-

sonous waste from the system of this enormous creature; absorbed first by the infinitely ramifying, thread-like ducts gathering at their sensitive terminals matter destructive to its life, hurrying it to millions of small intestines, to be collected in turn by larger, flowing to the great sewer, on to the drainage canal, and finally to the ocean. This ten thousand acres of flesh-like tissue is again knit and inter-knit with a nervous system marvelously complete, delicate filaments for hearing, knowing, almost feeling the pulse of its organism, acting upon the ligaments and tendons for motive impulse, in all flowing the impelling fluid of man's own life. Its nerve ganglia!—The peerless Corliss tandems whirling their hundred ton fly-wheels, fed by gigantic rows of water tube boilers burning oil, a solitary man slowly pacing backward and forward, regulating here and there the little feed valves controlling the deafening roar of the flaming gas, while beyond, the incessant clicking, dropping, waiting—lifting, waiting, shifting of the governor gear controlling these modern Goliaths seems a visible brain in intelligent action, registered infallibly in the enormous magnets, purring in the giant embrace of great induction coils, generating the vital current meeting with instant response in the rolling cars on elevated tracks ten miles away, where the glare of the Bessemer steel converter makes a conflagration of the clouds. More quietly still, whispering down the long, low rooms of factory buildings buried in the gloom beyond, range on range of stanch, beautifully perfected automatons, murmur contentedly with occasional click-clack, that would have the American manufacturing industry of five years ago by the throat to-day; manipulating steel as delicately as a mystical shuttle of the modern loom manipulates a silk thread in the shimmering pattern of dainty gown. And the heavy breathing, the murmuring, the clangor, and the roar!—how the voice of this monstrous thing, this greatest of machines, a great city, rises to proclaim the marvel of the units of its structure, the ghastly warning boom from the deep throats of vessels heavily seeking inlet to the waterway below, answered by the echoing clangor of the bridge bells growing nearer and more ominous as the vessels cut momentarily from the flow of the nearer artery, warning the current from the swinging bridge now closing on its stately passage, just in time to receive the rush of steam, as a streak of light, the avalanche of blood and metal hurled across it and gone, roaring into the night on its glittering bands of steel, ever faithfully encircled by the slender magic lines tick-tapping in invincible protection.[11]

This was a nightmare world where man, machine, and city had truly merged, and the description pursues its labyrinthine way through a landscape that alternates between being the human body, a factory, a machine, and the city itself. The Vitruvian man had gone berserk, since the male body had become a machine for production. There was no perspective outside this, and no escape from the logic of its continual self reproduction. You can see this development in the history of science, where man increasingly becomes a mechanism to be operated upon, in the literature of *Frankenstein* and *Germinal*,[12] and in the politics of war and peace, where mechanization increasingly takes control. The very idea of humanity, the proudest achievement of Enlightenment logic, disappeared into the logic of mechanical reproduction, which turns all of man into no more than a potential part of the machine.[13] Space and place, and with them the traditional notion of a human being, disappeared in the modern city.

What was the alternative to this world? It was the retreat fashioned by women in the nooks, crannies, and interiors of the city. The middle-class interior became the mirror of the outside world, collecting its pieces and framing them in a way that could make sense. If men made the city, middle-class women made the city their own. They created havens within the city that allowed them to define themselves in urban terms while contemplating its forces at a remove.

The first principle of the middle-class interior was that it was resolutely not the faceless desert of the city. It clothed itself in the fashions of the rich.[14] The contours of the interior world were based on three elements. First, the appearance of things there was defined by the cycles of fashion that had become the dominant definers of the spaces the wealthy inhabited in the eighteenth century. Second, the interior was in between. It defined the in-between character of the middle class—in between the idle aristocracy and the working class, in between the isolated palace or castle and the apartment or hovel, and always constructed precariously and self-consciously as a new place—as it emerged in the nineteenth century. Third, the interior derived its motive force from the particular way in which women were assigned the role of defining this new middle-class culture, much in the way women had been assigned the role of cultivating and domesticating space, objects, and people controlled by men since the Middle Ages.

Figure 7.8: A. Kappis,
Closet, Villa Berg, **1855**

The elements of the middle-class interior were the various permutations of classical architecture, including the baroque, rococo, and neoclassical styles. Just as the École des Beaux-Arts simplified the use of columns and organizational principles, so the logic of the marketplace created versions of these grand orders that were more flexible. On wallpaper you could have any combination of pilasters and friezes you might desire. Inside the house or apartment a chair that could have seated Louis XIV could coexist with draperies in the style of Percier and Fontaine. As the cycles of fashion sped up to keep track with the cycles of production, moreover, it became important to be able to come up with ever more combinations and variations on these historical styles.[15] The style known as Regency in England was the last of the more or less pure classical domestic architectures. After that it became hard to tell the curving moldings from the reduced straight chair back. It all blended into a vaguely formal, vaguely classical environment. The very fact that strict rules were broken, combinations that would invalidate the carefully constructed statement were ignored, and the scale and material of these elements were changed took the architecture away from its function as imposing a clear order on the world. This was, as architects hasten to point out to this day, a kind of bastard architecture that appropriated the forms of buildings but divorced them from the logic of both planned and abstract order and from the logic of construction. This was a world of flexible images that you could manipulate at will.

Figure 7.9: T.L.S. Rowbotham,
Morning Room, Leigh Court, **1845**

The stew became even richer as non-Western and nonclassical forms of architecture begin to enter the picture. Chinoiserie and neo-Gothicism had been a vogue in the eighteenth century, but in the nineteenth century they become accepted styles with their own rationale. If in the eighteenth century Horace Walpole had delighted in the nostalgia of his neo-Gothic country house, Strawberry Hill, then in the nineteenth century theorists like A.W.N. Pugin and John Ruskin argued that the neo-Gothic offered a concrete alternative to the city. They wanted to carve a medieval community of work and prayer out of the wicked chartered streets of the city in order to re-create a simpler and more communal way of life. The proponents and designers of neo-Gothic interiors saw them as places where the middle-class family could connect to craft, eschewing the aggressive distance of classical architecture.[16] Similarly, Oriental forms became commentaries on the closed prospects of colonial society, opening up new social possibilities at the very same time that the models for these spaces were being destroyed by the enterprise that was at the heart of the middle-class engine of growth. The exotic (and erotic) textures, materials, and forms were a ready-made critique of capitalist society, imported into the heart of that society as innocuous objects of consumption.[17]

That critique became increasingly self-conscious as the century went on, but initially all the revivals and importations were just rages, crazes, and fashions. Removing herself from categories of judgment, the middle-class woman was free to choose a world for herself from whatever she could afford. The result was an often luscious environment in which things accumulated instead of being selected. There was an emphasis on surfaces, textures, and colors. Deep, dark and saturated, highly figured, and layered—these were the main attributes of the oriental rugs, heavily stuffed chairs, deeply carved oak chests, and heavy curtains. Against this background, Chinese vases, gilt frames, and delicate serving utensils would stand out. Emerging out of this collage of forms would be paintings, often of exotic scenes, or mirrors that doubled the riches.

The domestic middle-class interior was a padded version of the Dutch seventeenth-century space of the home, and the paintings of that period became popular again at that time. This revival represented the paradoxical nature of the middle-class interior for women. On the one hand, it was a place of domestic virtue, a place where cleanliness, craft, and the order of everyday life created an alternative to the wide-open spaces and exclusionary orders of the outside. On the other hand, it was a place of fantasy, in which women could lose themselves in a sensuous delight. These two qualities were also negative: The woman was both imprisoned in domestic chores and an abject object of desire that could not assert its own reality.

Figure 7.10: Owen Jones, *Patterns in the Chinese Style,* from *The Grammar of Ornament,* 1856

The space of women then became the space of desire and family. As such it formed the core of middle-class economy and its ideology. Because the woman took care of reproduction, the man could engage in production away from the home. The home became the isolated place where the body was nourished and children were raised. It was zoned for domesticity. The home also became the core of consumption, the place that absorbed, displayed, ordered, and used all the objects the men produced. The home became both the limit of desire and the place of desire. It was the home base from which the conquests of space, race, and class took place. It also became the dream that justified work, the home that used up all of the family's resources, and the treasure house of both objects and sex.

To accomplish this, the interior had certain characteristics. First, it had to be isolated. Not only was it the sacred space of the family, but it was also a harem. Multiple doors, degrees of publicness in different rooms, heavy curtains, and even the many objects of storage accomplished this. Second, it had

Figure 7.12 Alfred Waterhouse, Reception Room, Eaton Hall, Cheshire, 1882

to be full. The room became a collection that mirrored, defined, and displayed the status of the family. Third, it had to be soft and sensuous, an extension of the way in which the woman's body appeared to the man. Fourth, it had to be conscious of its place within a larger order. The middle-class interior was in between high architecture and the informal spaces of everyday activities. Fifth, it had to be a place of acculturation or of what one critic has called "artifactual literacy,"[18] where the daily ritual of eating, sleeping, and even playing was made part of the assimilation and reproduction of the orders that defined this space.

In an 1877 painting by J. J. Tissot you can see this space. The women of the family are at home. The mother slouches low in a chair, reading a newspaper that connects her to an outside world we see only as light, shadows, and a few leaves. The curtains are almost drawn, the woman sits beneath a mirror that doubles the objects around her, and she is hemmed in by heavy couches. The children play between rugs and tiger skins, creating their own way through the layers of soft surfaces that seem to drown the room. Each object speaks of other, sensuous worlds that exist somewhere else but are represented here only for their texture, their feel, their aura. There is an air of stillness, as if the incessant movement that makes the space of the exterior such an active one has been smothered by the inward turn. Between all these materials and messages, the children play hide-and-seek, trying to find a path for themselves in this parlor.

Figure 7.13 James Tissot, *Hide and Seek*, 1877

The middle-class domestic interior was a place of interiority, a place where you turned back to yourself, rather than appear on the stage of the world. Even more than the Dutch seventeenth-century interior, it was a place closed off from the surrounding world, where multiple orders, colors, forms, and actions created a confusing labyrinth. Here everything had its place, everything could be seen, everything could be known, and by extension, everything could be made.

It was an odd kind of order and an even stranger kind of making, however. It was the order that comes out of the way a floor was cleaned, teacups were stored, clothes were laid out, and chairs were arranged. Each order represented a ritual, wealth, and one's place in the world. By knowing what fork to use and where or how to sit, you defined your place in the world. You inhabited it and made it your own. By cooking, child rearing, and cleaning, you continually remade that world, but only as a version of what it already was. The domestic interior was a condensed mirror of the outside world, where the woman made real and inhabitable the grand designs of the fast-growing city of industry.

The interior as mirror also means that it was a place of beauty. It was a place where you looked at yourself and defined yourself through your objects. The border between your body, your clothes, your jewelry, your cutlery, your furniture, and your paintings or mirrors became increasingly hard to find. It was all just layers of beauty. You lost yourself in a material world where everything turned to itself, mirroring itself in answering patterns.

The ideal middle-class space was a lavish, all-enveloping one. In 1897 Henry James wrote *The Spoils of Poynton*. In it he describes Poynton, the house of the formidable Mrs. Gereth, as it appeared to the appreciative Fleda Vetch:

> Wandering through clear chambers where the general effect made preferences almost as impossible as if they had been shocks, pausing at open doors where vistas were long and grand she would, even if she had not already known, have discovered for herself that Poynton was the record of a life. It was written in great syllables of colour and form, the tongues of other countries and the hands of rare artists. It was all France and Italy, with their ages composed to rest. For England you looked out of old windows—it was England that was the wide embrace. While outside, on the low terraces, she contradicted gardeners and refined on nature, Mrs. Gereth left her guest to finger fondly the brasses that Louis Quinze might have thumbed, to sit with Venetian velvets just held in a loving palm, to hang over cases of enamels and pass and repass before cabinets. There were not many pictures—the panels and the stuffs were themselves the picture; and in all the great wainscoted house there was not an inch of pasted paper. What struck Fleda most in it was the high pride of her friend's taste, a fine arrogance, a sense of style which, however, amused and amusing, never compromised or stooped.[19]

Poynton was more than a house or even the mirror of its collector-inhabitant: It typified a world view that constructed itself out of objects, arranged according to use and narrative and composed by the dictates of style that was so personal and ephemeral that it could never be written. One either saw it, or one didn't, and Fleda—and Henry James—made it their business and passion to see.

What they saw was a world that was collected. It was not built, constructed, or ordered, but assembled, arranged, composed, and decorated. This world was the domain of women, not men. It was a world where nothing was made and often not even much was said. These houses were made up not merely of functional rooms but of a concatenation of spaces that flowed, undulated, and enveloped you. It was a space of culture, class, and appearance, but also of privacy and comfort. The two worked in tandem: By keeping up appearances, a woman could make a space of her own, and by claiming that she was only defining herself by surrounding herself with objects that represented her discriminating taste, the woman could present a fitting image.

Unfortunately there was an inherent uneasiness about such homes. They were designed in bastardized versions of the styles first of the eighteenth and later of earlier centuries, they denied their uses and sites, and they tried to deny the very facts of middle-class life. They presented an image of the middle-class woman and her life as a fantasy. There was nothing real, authentic, or truly familiar about them. Either they were doomed to become museums imprisoning their inhabitants, or they would be just pale reflections of some imagined ideal. In contrast with the almost ethereal vision of Poynton, for instance, stands the more ordinary and real place of exile to which Mrs. Gereth finds herself removed by her son's marriage:

> Mrs. Gereth hated such windows, the one flat glass, sliding up and down, especially when they enjoyed a view of four iron pots on pedestals, painted white and containing ugly geraniums, ranged on the edge of the gravel path and doing their best to give it the air of a terrace. Fleda had instantly averted her eyes from these ornaments, but Mrs. Gereth grimly gazed, wondering of course how a place in the deepest depth of Essex and three miles from a small station could contrive to look so suburban. The room was practically a shallow box, with the junction of the walls and ceiling guiltless of curve or cornice and marked merely by the little band

of crimson paper glued round the top of the other paper, a turbid gray sprigged with silver flowers. This decoration was rather new and quite fresh; and there was in the centre of the ceiling a big square beam papered over in white, as to which Fleda hesitated about venturing to remark that it was rather picturesque. She recognized in time that this remark would be weak and that, throughout, she should be able to say nothing either for the mantelpieces or for the doors, of which she saw her companion become sensible with a soundless moan. On the subject of doors especially Mrs. Gereth had the finest views: the thing in the world she most despised was the meanness of the single flap. From end to end, at Poynton, there were high double leaves. At Ricks the entrances to the rooms were like the holes of rabbit-hutches.[20]

What was wrong with this set of rooms was everything that in fact made the middle-class interior possible. The advances in technology that permitted large panes of glass and allowed for the mass production of wallpaper let light and simple, repetitive decoration enter rooms. The growth in population and the proliferation in rooms made for houses that appeared mass-produced. Simple, functional design led designers to do away with moldings, double leaves, and curves. Ricks is a suburban settlement, one that encapsulates the bare bones of bourgeois life without the romantic illusions of a great home to which Poynton aspires. By the end of the book Poynton has gone up in smoke, and all the characters are forced to lead their more or less conventional middle-class lives.

This is the dilemma of the middle-class interior. On the one hand, it was a place that was a marvel of technology, filled with all the machinery that created comfort and allowed people to live in isolation. On the other hand, it was a place of fantasy, another world opened up within the increasingly harsh and confusing realities of the city. It was a place that could exist only by defining the woman as the image of fantasy and making her dependent on an alien technology. The resulting realities created a new stage for women, a place that was potentially empowering and imprisoning, a place of their own that was tied to the networks of change, a place that was both isolated and allowed women to create a new world.

The suffocating possibilities of the interior become obvious in Eastman Johnson's 1872 painting *Not at Home*. The scene is a domestic parlor, filled with paintings, antique chairs, knickknacks on a sideboard, and rugs. The dark wood moldings and ponderous walls weigh down on the room. The woman is not at the center of this picture, enjoying her domestic delights. She can be glimpsed at the side, creeping up the staircase to escape the burden of social obligations of the weekly ritual in which a woman had to receive visitors "at home."

In 1892 Charlotte Perkins Gilman, a pioneering feminist who wrote *The Man-made World,*[21] wrote the harrowing tale, "The Yellow Wallpaper."[22] In it the sensitive woman is imprisoned in her room by her husband doctor, who believes that science teaches him that all exposure to the rigors of the outside world (which were supposed to be therapeutic for men) are dangerous for women. Inside the woman sinks ever further into despair and into the spiraling inward motion of the space, until she can do no more than rip away at the paper, gnaw at her bedstead, and completely internalize her imprisonment. We last see her sidled next to the devastated wallpaper in the room she has stripped of all but her tied-down bedstead.

Figure 7.14: Eastman Johnson, *Not at Home*, c. 1872

This is the end of the proliferation of the feminine space of the rococo. The luxurious elaboration of the space that men had given upper-class and later middle-class women had turned into a tomb where the woman is buried underneath the proliferation of the image of her.

It is important to realize that the cult of the domestic interior fixes the modern definition of femininity. Once enclosed in the interior, the woman made a place for herself. Men then associated this space with femininity. Women had no choice but to accept this role. Beyond that a capitalist economy developed a *raison d'être* for this space: It was the place of reproduction and education, as opposed to the male place of production and action, and it was the place of consumption, as opposed to production. It was a space of stasis, as opposed to the male world of continual movement and change. It was the place of the mirror, not the window, the place where a hard-won culture could define and live itself out. The domestic interior was the place of self-definition within the parameters of a rational and aggressively growing culture.

Figure 7.15: McKim, Mead and White, Hall, Newcomb House, Elberon, New Jersey, 1881

We derive much of our definitions of the roles of men and women from this space. Many people still believe that women should stay home to take care of the children, while men should engage in the productive (re)building of the outside world. We see the world of objects, surfaces, and beauty as the realm of women, while the nakedly abstract city is the place of men and power. We should remember that this is only because middle-class men and women were imitating a particular upper-class set of spaces and rituals, were engaging in consumption that justified the emergence of a capitalist economy, and were carving a space out for themselves that was an alternative to both the nondescript places of the poor or the places of pure appearance of the ruling class.

This in-between place soon found a location: the suburb. Originally envisioned by English theoreticians such as Ebenezer Howard as an ideal place, it became the hallmark of middle-class life. The idea was that the suburb could use all the systems of technology that allowed for the radically new and separate world of the middle class to appear—namely, the webs of streets, transportation systems, and later sewage, water, electricity, and gas—to let the reality of the city escape. The logic of such systems was in fact to destroy any sense of place. The connection with land or fixed orders was no longer necessary. In its place artificial worlds could be created. They would clothe themselves in an image of place, as if they were part of some validating nature that predated and rooted us. The suburb buried technology underneath thatched cottages, rambling rooms, gardens, and open space that elided the difference between public and private. Thus they avoided the game of representations and very real transformation of the city into a world of "dark Satanic mills" that so troubled critics from Blake to Marx. In the suburb you no longer had to walk down chartered streets. You could wander down picturesque paths that offered miniature versions of the estates of the rich. Finally the suburb turned the isolation of domestic and "productive" work into an urban fact by isolating the woman not just inside the home but inside a whole community that was far removed from the office buildings, factories, and empty civic spaces of the city.[23]

The city became the place of men, the suburb the place of women. Its urban plan made the curves of the rococo and the clothing in which women appeared to float through the unreal space of the interior into a fact that people had to walk through every day. The labyrinthine turns of the Dutch canals became cul-de-sacs, and the textured surfaces of the carpets became the "rusticated" brick, stone, shingle, and wood surfaces of the suburban cottage. This was a world that again turned in on itself and organized itself not around public spaces of appearance but around the annexes to the culture of consumption and reproduction—namely, the school and the shopping area. Only the train station provided a sense of civic architecture of the kind you could find in the city, and even it and whatever modest town hall, library, or other civic structure existed were designed to blend in with the image of a domesticated landscape.[24]

Men in particular conquered and shaped America, but then women filled it in and fleshed it out into a feminine domain. Yet the places where women lived were not the places where decisions were made in important buildings. We still live with the results of that distinction: Most suburban environments are not planned logically, in terms of either convenience or land use, but rather create the most convincing romance of being another place for the least amount of money and at the farthest remove from the centers of power.

If you were not a middle-class woman, your choices were even fewer. You could either work in a factory or take work in at home, if you were not busy taking care of what few meager spaces remained to you. There was no chance for escape, no space for the creation of an alternative world.

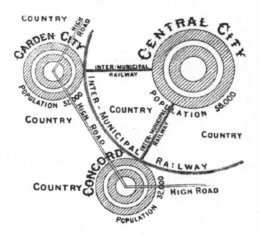

Figure 7.16: Ebenezer Howard, *Garden City Diagram*, 1902

Figure 7.17: Raymond Unwin,
English Village, 1909

Your only choice was to become part of the spectacle of the city by roaming the world of nightclubs and restaurants. Here men and women were seemingly free in a world of abundance, of indeterminate space, and of shifting appearances, where the impressions one caught in a mirror were not of one's self but of a continually changing composition of forms, colors, and textures into which all inhabitants were dissolving. It was the truly new world of which the French impressionist painters were so enamored, where acting out, buying, drifting through an artificial world, and delighting in your separation from reality were nervous ideals.[25]

Thus a new space opened up in the city. Between glass and steel, spaces flowed and were reflected in windows and mirrors. Here men and women mixed, and all people could construct their own identities. This city of self-

Figure 7.18: Henri Toulouse-Lautrec,
Au Moulin Rouge, 1895

construction first appeared in shopping arcades or passages that started cutting through London, Paris, and Berlin at the beginning of the century. These were spaces that dissolved the fixed and closed orders of the block and opened up an unreal space of thin membranes of steel, supporting glass that kept the sun and the rain out but did not act so much as a barrier as a transforming lens. Here morals fell apart, as women of high economic and social standing could mix with prostitutes. Here everything was available and possible, including a fluidity of social positions and the availability of new goods. Here a new world was born.[26]

The space of the arcade became the space of the department store, an open grid of glass and steel that again dissolved the certainties of stone monuments and invited women back into the city to shop in a version of the rational environments in which men worked and made decisions. The great department stores, with their skylights, elevators, garish displays of goods, and confusing spaces, offered an interior world blown up into a collage of goods that had little use for the orders of architecture. You could say the same of some of the

Figure 7.19: Owen Jones, *Osler's Shop*, London, 1860

other spaces in which women reentered the city: The theaters and operas, where both actors and audiences engaged in theatrics, were not just dark boxes with one shape but, like the Paris Opéra, designed by Jean-Louis-Charles Garnier in 1867, grew into stairs, porte cochères, ramps, windows, balconies, restaurants, lounges, bridges, and the whole menu of forms that dissected and proliferated spatial possibilities. They broke the rules of a proper architectural space, with its clear axis and hierarchy of functions, in favor of a delight in the infinite possibility of a tapestry of interpenetrating spaces that had more to do with the arrangement of the domestic interior than with the rules of public architecture. Restaurants and bars continued this dissolution of monumental certainty into spaces of ephemerality and hedonism.

It was exciting and dangerous for women to come to the city. Not only were they entering into a realm that was not theirs and was full of possibility, but the forms they encountered there were both confusing and exciting. The new spaces of middle-class spectacle opened new vistas for them, and they sought to make them their own. They sought to bring to the wilds of the city the domestic virtues they had been trained to develop at home. Thus the city became the very embodiment of the struggle for power between men and women, played out in terms of how the city should work, appear, and grow:

> With the coming of "modernity" the cities of veiled women have ceded to cities of spectacle and voyeurism, in which women, while seeking and sometimes finding the freedom of anonymity, are often all too visible. They are in fact a part of the spectacle, and the kaleidoscope of city life becomes intensely contradictory for women. Commerce, consumerism and pleasure seduce them into its thoroughfares, yet men and the state continue their attempts to confine them to the private sphere or to the safety of certain zones. Since the Industrial Revolution a deadly struggle has been waged over women's presence in cities.[27]

Women entering the city brought with them a system of values that led them to take part in some of the most significant urban reform movements of the end of the century. As Gunther Barth has pointed out, when women came to the Meccas of consumerism, they also found slums and filthy streets.[28] They found empty orders that were not easy to live in. Some of them joined with reform-minded designers and politicians to beautify the city, and thus, for instance, the American City Beautiful movement was born. It aimed to clean up politics as well as space and saw that as one activity: Clean streets, livable tenements, parks and sewage lines, governed by bureaucrats in myriad systems of diffused power, rather than by autocratic men, would turn the whole city into a version of the safe domestic environment women created for their families in the suburbs.[29]

Critics were more ambivalent about what they thought was the feminization of the city. They had always had a suspicion that the city they controlled was not as purely their realm as they would have liked to believe. The city became the place where orders continued to fall apart and where morality was questioned; it was always a threat to their authority and sense of place. That was true on two levels. First, the women reformers sought to create a kind of suburban utopia. Second, women who were not middle-class filled the street with the reality of poverty, dislocation, and the flesh. As recently as the 1960s Daniel Patrick Moynihan could claim that the problems of the inner cities in America were the result of black households without men leading them.[30] The loose woman, bringing up children by herself, stood as a rebuke to the male order of things. She was making the kind of place that defined femininity, but she was doing it without male control. Prostitutes were the extreme example of this case. These "women of loose morals" and "streetwalkers" uncoupled themselves from the twin anchors of the middle-class state: the defining environment and the value system of work, frugality, monogamy, religious belief, and asceticism that went with it. They were loose women in the purest sense of the word: They were loose from the bounds of a moralized space.[31]

It is amazing how space and morality were bound up in the middle-class city. The city was meant to be clean, as were the minds of its inhabitants. It was meant to be made up of parts that each had one function, just as the bodies and tools of its inhabitants were meant to find their callings and stay in them, have sex only for procreation, and serve a greater good by doing their own particular tasks. The ideal city was no longer a utopia out there but was the city of commerce cleaned of all of its vices. It had turned into an unreal place

Figure 7.20: Jean-Louis-Charles Garnier, Paris Opéra, Lobby, 1875

of glass, steel, cleanliness, lack of lust, and lack of real bodies. Thus the modernist ideal was born out of the belief that the world could be remade because the whole world could be brought into the process of continual production and reproduction.

The problem was that the woman remained a real person, just as the man could not live in the abstract places of power he ordained. The woman was made of flesh and blood and was often not a virgin. The real place of the new city was one in which the grids of glass and steel became department stores, theaters, and arcades, in which real women filled the new streets and strolled through the lawns, finally peering nonchalantly over their shoulders in Manet's famous painting. They were here, in all their flesh and blood.

The city, in the image of some critics, still represents this dilemma. For all of our desire to think of it as the new place, the in-between realm of pure rationality, and the logical result of the processes of production and consumption, it is still a real place with smells and textures. The city becomes a labyrinth that envelops you as you move through it. You are always inside it. The city, always personified as a woman, becomes the space where woman is realized in a profoundly problematic way. She becomes spatial reality, the real domesticated and the ongoing work of reproduction turned into an inescapable and all-encompassing reality.

8

AT HOME IN THE MAELSTROM OF MODERNITY

ONE WOMAN WHO TOOK THINGS INTO HER OWN HANDS WAS CATHARINE BEECHER. A member of a powerful family that included her sister the author Harriet Beecher Stowe and her father, the Reverend Lyman Beecher, she cowrote *The American Woman's Home*.[1] She intended the short text as a manual that a middle-class woman of limited means but grand ambitions could use to make a place for herself and her family. The resulting house would look like every American single-family home, only more so. It would be like a child's drawing of a home, a memory of the upright stance that reminded us of our ability to make something that stood in the world, of the spreading roof that contained the spaces we had made, and of the chimney that showed us where we could find the hearth that drew us to the place. Porches that served as miniatures of the suburban situation—which is to say that they were open spaces that re-created a domesticated version of nature—would then soften the hard edges of this vision. This was the American home to which we all should aspire.

Figure 8.11: Catharine Beecher and Harriet Beecher Stowe, *A Christian Home*, from *The American Woman's Home*, 1869

The inside was a more radical space. The ground floor was basically two large, flexible rooms. Only the chimney, which sat in the middle of the space so that it could heat most of the house, was fixed. As in the work of Frank Lloyd Wright, it was the vertical pivot around which domesticity spread out. The way Beecher and Stowe proposed dividing the space was startling: Closets that doubled as walls could move, fold out, turn, and otherwise create spaces for storage, for reading, for educating the children, or for working. The house could have two large, relatively undifferentiated rooms, or it could have many specialized spaces.[2]

The kitchen, on the other hand, was a place of great specificity and small square footage. Here the model was a ship's galley. Beecher did her own analysis of the actual work of cooking and arrived at a layout that would make this place as efficient as possible. In it the woman would merge with the act of preparing and cooking food.[3]

The two hallmarks of the house were simplicity and efficiency. This was not a place for display, nor was it just whatever space was left over. Beecher and Stowe carried the sense of careful construction through into the design of every piece of furniture and even the picture frames. They showed how a housewife could make most of these things herself, using simple materials and all the skills of composing that were, she believed, innate in the American middle-class woman. The result would be pieces that not only would be cheap and sturdy but also would represent the woman's ability to create a moral world:

> In the Divine Word it is written, "The wise woman buildeth her house." To
> be "wise," is "to choose the best means for accomplishing the best end."
> It has been shown that the best end for a woman to seek is the training
> of God's children for their eternal home, by guiding them to intelligence,
> virtue, and true happiness. When, therefore, the wise woman seeks a
> home in which to exercise this ministry, she will aim to secure a house so
> planned that it will provide in the best manner for health, industry, and
> economy, those cardinal requisites of domestic enjoyment and success.
> To aid in this, is the object of the following drawings and descriptions,

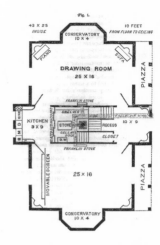

Figure 8.2: Catharine Beecher and Harriet Beecher Stowe, *First Floor Plan*, from *The American Woman's Home*, 1869

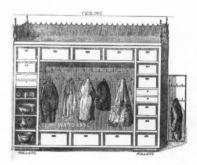

Figure 8.3: Catharine Beecher and Harriet Beecher Stowe, *Closet*, from *The American Woman's Home*, 1869

which will illustrate a style of living more conformed to the great design for which the family is instituted than that which ordinarily prevails among those classes which take the lead in forming the customs of society. The aim will be to exhibit modes of economizing labor, time, and expenses, so as to secure health, thrift, and domestic happiness to persons of limited means, in a measure rarely attained even by those who possess wealth. At the head of this chapter is a sketch of what may be properly called a Christian house; that is, a house contrived for the express purpose of enabling every member of a family to labor with the hands for the common good, and by modes at once healthful, economical and tasteful.[4]

This plan had a political dimension as well: Beecher and Stowe foresaw building the prototype of such houses in the uplands of North Carolina, a rural area that the enlightened North had just won for free and rational civilization by the Civil War. The American woman's home was a specific, real version of what Beecher saw as an ideal space. It was a place where women could build a world in which everything made sense, everything was used, and everything revolved around the reproduction of such a sense of order in the children or in the further expansion of the house. You could argue, of course, that this order was just a sublimation of the space of male power that the woman traced as she dusted and swept.[5] Yet it also offered an alternative to this world. If the world of men was made up of palaces and factories, office buildings, and the empty spaces of public gathering, then the space of women could be something other than a retreat from that world. It could be a miniaturization of the modern environment, a place where the artificiality of the man-made world was made conscious and real. Living in Beecher's house, you could make the modern world your own.

The idea that we should take charge of, assimilate, and perhaps become an active part of the processes of modernization was, of course, not one Beecher and Stowe just invented. The École des Beaux-Arts itself had been shaken since 1848 with revolts by students who thought that architecture should give form to the new materials, types of buildings, and processes of building that were rapidly transforming the world. To architects such as Henri Labrouste, however, the modern world was one to be organized and contained by architecture. The role of architecture was to find an abstract system of order that would be powerful enough to contain the machine, the metropolis, steel and glass, and every other phenomenon man might invent. Labrouste was not interested in weaving together a world out of moments of change, revelations of newness, and liberation from the bonds of the old. He wanted to build the brave new world according to his own specifications, just as the Renaissance architects had imagined a new world four centuries earlier.[6]

While architects were worried about how to give shape to the great new forces of the modern world, technology was changing the way we experienced our environments in ways architects could neither predict nor control. Electricity, the telephone, sewage, and such more intangible forces as mass marketing were dissolving the barriers of space and time to such an extent that architects' attempts to control life seemed increasingly inadequate. Yet men controlled the mechanisms of mechanization, and as a result, the advances in science and technology somehow managed to perpetuate the place of women. As Ruth Schwartz Cowan has pointed out:

> Before industrialization, women fed, clothed, and nursed their families by preparing (with the help of their husbands and children) food, clothing, and medication. In the post-industrial age, women feed, clothe and nurse their families (without much direct assistance from anyone else) by cooking, cleaning, driving, shopping and waiting. The nature of work has changed, but the goal is still there and so is the necessity for time-consuming labor. Technological systems that might have truly eliminated the labor of housewives could have been built, but such systems have been eliminated from the home as well.[7]

Instead of the communal kitchens and flowing open spaces of which individuals dreamed, we created a world of washing machines, day-care centers, and other innovations that only bound women to a new form of technological structure. Even the design of appliances was gender-coded, so that the ones women used had softer lines and were made to appear less threatening, while power tools, cars, and the outsides of house remained harder-edged, more forbidding, and what we still think of as more masculine.

The struggle for the soul of the designed environment in this century is thus not between things that look modern and things that look old-fashioned but between attempts to use technology to liberate us and the use of new tools for the same old games of bondage. If modernist architects created the more liberating designs, it was only because their choice of forms that looked new already removed them one step from the standard identifications that placed us in our respective sexual positions in home and office, inside and outside, comfortable world and gridded place of meaning.

Much of what we know today as modernist architecture has its roots in ways of thinking that enshrine male power in the buildings we inhabit. When we walk through the clean, empty, and soulless spaces of our office buildings, shopping malls, parking garages, or airports, we are in environments that are meant to reflect a science of efficiency that has determined that there should be only as much building there as is needed to perform a particular task. The surfaces of our spaces are equally clean of any decoration or seeming representation because such elements would only add unnecessary complications. The idea is that modernist architecture reduces itself to the task of building the world that works, the world that replaces all reality with man's creation. How we live within that order is of secondary importance. In the end such spaces create empty prisms of power and prisons of efficiency in which we have few choices.

Beecher and those who thought like her, however, had another idea. They believed that we could use the tools out of which we built a human culture to create a world that was flexible, was adaptable, and would represent the fact that we ourselves were making that world. It would be a world that worked in many ways and would show you how it worked. Seeing would be knowing would be making.

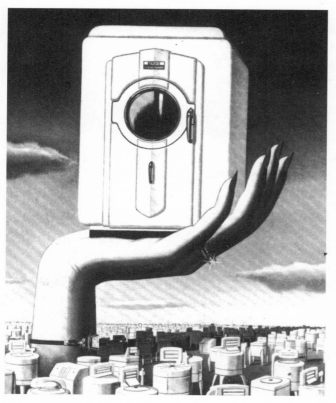

Figure 8.4: Advertisement for the Bendix Automatic Washer, 1947

The great theorist of this attitude was the English critic John Ruskin. In his "The Two Paths in Art,"[8] which at one point was the most widely read text on design in America,[9] he had a vision of what was wrong with our society and how we could change it. Instead of the factories that were mass-producing goods, we needed crafts that would allow us each to make our own objects of everyday use. Instead of the large cities and inhuman spaces of London, Manchester, or Liverpool, we needed small communities where people would define their spaces themselves. Finally, instead of an art that imposed an abstract aesthetics on the objects and spaces we used, we needed an art that would draw out and compose the inherent qualities of the materials at hand, including the new ones only just being discovered, and allow them to reveal their own nature. We would learn, he said, from the interior. We are entering, he said, "a period of our world's history in which domestic life, aided by the arts of peace, will slowly, but at last entirely, supersede public life and the arts of war."[10]

The communal world Ruskin envisioned was not all that different from the one that Thomas Jefferson imagined for his beloved Virginia, and it also resembled the utopias of such anarchist thinkers as Prince Peter Kropotkin.[11] This would be a world that people would create together, in which power and man-made spaces would dissolve into continually changing networks of connection. Imagine living in a small community where your work is the continual building of the spaces and objects all around you. Agriculture, craft, building, and politics would merge into a continual activity of remaking the world around you.[12] Some people tried to build such worlds. Tolstoy created a small cooperative community on his estate, and William Morris built communal craft ventures in rural England. It was in America, though, that large numbers of people sought to build such communities.[13]

These utopias were based on the idea that it was the function of the community, not the woman, to cook, clean, and take care of children. The spaces where this would take place could be large kitchens that resembled those of the early monasteries or glassed-in courtyards that spoke of the freedom of the arcades. They would be places that would not impose a hierarchical order on people but would be covered, in many cases, with an endless proliferation of colonnades that were open on all ends. This was a flexible space where anything could happen and everybody was free to construct his or her own relationships with others in an ordered and organized universe.

There were frightening tendencies to this utopian vision, of course. You could also see the colony of free love of the Oneida Community as a protofascist world in which nobody except the central leader had any power and where there was no place to hide from Big Brother. The freedom of the rational utopia was an artificial and circumscribed one. It depended on the suppression of the individual, of material, of texture, and of all the vagaries and inconsistencies of everyday life. Yet it was also an exhilarating one that spoke of the possibility of building a new world together. It is a world that still lives in a few isolated instances, such as in the Israeli kibbutz.

It was also a utopia that existed more thoroughly in arts and crafts than in lived environments. As the communities fell apart one after another, the workshops, working methods, and objects inspired by Ruskin continued to flourish. The Arts and Crafts style, as it came to be known in English-speaking countries, rejected the cycles of style in favor of forms that revealed both the history of their making and their use. A piece of furniture designed by Gustav Stickley, for instance, should show you how the wood had been cut and how the pieces were assembled. Every piece would be where it was and of the shape it was because of its use. A home designed according to Arts and Crafts principles would be a place where nothing was out of place, but also a place that was incomplete. All the forms and arrangements were of necessity fragmentary, to be woven together into a sensible (in both senses of that word) arrangement by the community of users.[14]

Pretty soon, however, it also became a style that was itself mass-produced and was a brief craze, before being cycled back into the history of novelty items that kept flooding the consumer market. It was kept alive only by a few artists and artisans in communes in Glasgow, Vienna, and Darmstadt. Instead, the image of the new became the flowing lines of art nouveau or Jugendstil, a revival of rococo images of femininity that were now meant to represent the continuous free flow of glass, steel, and modernity itself. Space dissolved into the continuous arcs of Victor Horta, leaving few spaces one could make one's own. A new nature was under construction, and to make it "natural," designers tried to make it flowing, organic, and feminine. Instead of seeing all the connections, you would just accept the inevitability of the victory of an age of steel and glass and go with the flow.

If you look at twentieth-century architecture and design, you can see that it has two wellsprings: the creation of a space of revelation and the creation of a space of dissolution. Both melded into the modern spaces we live in today, but the impulses are very different. One seeks to build a world that we can keep remaking. It asks us, ultimately, to make a space for ourselves that includes a new definition of who we are as human beings. The second seeks to transform us into necessary parts of a vast new mechanistic universe, while keeping alive only the image of what it means to be human. The first implies that we have to construct our own sexuality, the second that we have to live out the roles given to us as men and women.

The experimental station for the creation of both of these worlds was the Bauhaus. What started as a school for applied arts and crafts in 1919 eventually became a place where some of the greatest artists, architects, and designers—including women—of the century developed new ways of making spaces and objects that promised to give a lie to the restrictive methods of traditional art making. When Henry Clemens van de Velde founded the school, he was thinking very clearly in the tradition of Arts and Crafts. Both he and his successor, Walter Gropius,

Figure 8.5: Victor Horta, Staircase, Hôtel van Eetvelde, Brussels, 1895

hoped to see a cooperative commune of makers adapting the latest technology to the creation of new forms. As Gropius put it:

> In the conviction that household appliances and furnishings must be rationally related to each other, the Bauhaus is seeking—by systematic practical and theoretical research in the formal, technical and economic fields—to derive the design of an object from its natural functions and relationships. Modern man, who no longer dresses in historical garments but wears modern clothes, also needs a modern home appropriate to him and his time, equipped with all the modern devices of daily use. . . . The Bauhaus workshops are essentially laboratories in which prototypes of products suitable for mass production and typical of our time are carefully developed and constantly improved. In these laboratories the Bauhaus wants to train a new kind of collaborator for industry and the crafts, who has an equal command of both technology and form.[15]

The idea was that all crafts were part of building a new world, from tapestry to costume design to architecture. Gropius wanted to replace both the notion of style and the idea that design was something one imposed on the world with an art that would come out of the simplest shapes to transform the activities of everyday life. His mentor and inspiration was the architect Peter Behrens, who for many years worked with the largest industrial combine in Germany, AEG, to give a shape to every object and building it produced. He created a romance of industry that continued from the light bulb to the factory in which that light bulb was made, so that the romance of the new was made real in a seamless environment where the machine ruled over men and women.[16] Gropius hoped to extend this idea into society as a whole. What mattered was the construction of a new world, not the separate objects, activities, or sexes within it: "Let us then create a new guild of craftsmen without the class distinctions that raise an arrogant barrier between craftsman and artist! Together let us desire, conceive, and create the new structure of the future, which will embrace architecture and sculpture and painting in one unity and which will one day rise toward heaven from the hands of a million workers like the crystal symbol of a new faith."[17] As a result of this philosophy, all students at the Bauhaus learned about principles of design and order before they specialized in a particular field.

It took the more pragmatic Dutch painter Theo van Doesburg, who came to the Bauhaus in 1921 to give some extracurricular lectures, to provide the spatial dimension to this line of thinking. Though van Doesburg had cofounded the magazine and movement *De Stijl* with the theosophist Piet Mondrian, he was inclined to remind students that it mattered less what cosmic principles were to be found in geometry or color and more how such phenomena might help transform the world around them. Just as his three-dimensional work, such as the Café l'Aubette in Strasbourg, moved diagonal planes across walls, ceilings, and floors,

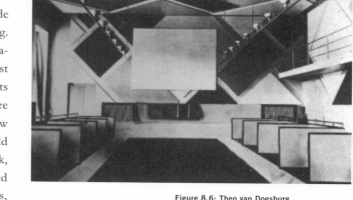

Figure 8.6: Theo van Doesburg, Café l'Aubette, Strasbourg, 1928

setting up a geometry of color that contradicted the staid relationships of orthogonal rooms, so he suggested that art in general could cut through and recombine the relationships of all spaces:

> The new architecture is formless and yet exactly defined; that is to say, it is not subject to any fixed aesthetic formal type. It has no mold (such as confectioners use) in which it produces the functional surfaces arising out of practical, living demands. In contradistinction to all earlier styles the new architectural methods know no closed type, no basic type. The functional space is strictly divided into rectangular surfaces having no individuality of their own. Although each one is fixed on the basis of the others, they may be visualized as extending infinitely.[18]

This became the fundamental doctrine of modernist art and craft: It believed that by breaking through the heavy walls, the static relationships of things to one another, and the layers of signification that made rooms the property of whoever was defining the style or message, and by replacing them with a dynamic, empty, functional, and technological advanced flow of space, modernists could break down the social and economic structures those staid structures represented. Modernism believed in movement, change, mutability, and transformation. It believed that we could build a better world by breaking our expectations of what the world around us looked like and how it worked.[19]

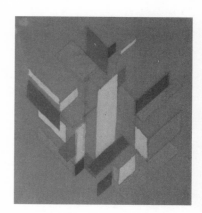

Figure 8.7: Theo van Doesburg, *Countercomposition in Primary Colors for the Maison de l'Artiste*, 1923

As such, modernism was a challenge not just to the social order but also to the division of the sexes. That was true not just because for almost the first time in Western European history women designers were accepted as (more or less) equal partners in this enterprise but because modernists sought to break through the whole hierarchy of spaces and plays of power of which the man-made environment was a reflection. Rather than the structures of separation and axes of conquest that buried and sublimated the spaces of gathering, they proposed neutral grids and spinning compositions. Instead of the narrative of function that assigned greater importance to the empty spaces of public appearance where the artificiality of male power was celebrated, they proposed flexible and nonsignificant spaces. Instead of the walls of fear and the roofs of shelter, they proposed new planes of possibility.

The Bauhaus itself became the embodiment of such principles. It was both a factory and a school, a place of gathering and a dormitory. It was a merger between the utopian models of the nineteenth century and the reality of modern production. Its white buildings formed L shapes and overlapping planes that interpenetrated and opened up, rather than assign a separate and hierarchically defined structure for each function. Inside, the objects of everyday use were part of the same design continuum. The tapestries by Anni Albers, the weavings by Gunta Stölzl, the chairs by Marcel Breuer, the teapots and silverware by Marianne Brandt all specified the interpenetration of planes as realizations of a technological progress that had no patience for the static divisions of the past.

Perhaps the most succinct statement of such principles was the Schröder-Schräder House, designed in 1924 by the Dutch furniture designer and architect Gerrit Rietveld. Often called a "three-dimensional Mondrian," it presented itself on the street as a decomposition of the heavy walls of the brick row houses to one side of it into the empty landscape of fields and irrigation ditches on the other side. This was no mere play of geometries, however. Some of the planes became ledges on which the client's son could lean as he talked to his visiting friends through an open window, while others replaced the usual relationship between ledge and sill, transom and wall with a sense of open and closed that was free to change with seasons and moods.

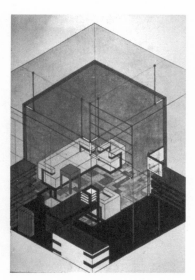

Figure 8.8: Walter Gropius, Director's Office, Bauhaus, Dessau, 1926

On the inside of the house, things really open up. Instead of a hearth, a stair-case with a skylight above it forms the center of the house. A trapdoor becomes a black plane that either opens or closes the possibility of vertical movement that spirals through the core of the house, combining your experi-ence of the space into a continuous movement. The top floor is the *piano nobile* of traditional architecture, but it is an open one. Movable walls allow it to become one large, multipurpose room or separate rooms for eating, sleeping, studying, or just looking out the windows that continue the space into the distance. Colored planes on all surfaces dissolve any association you might have with floor, ceiling, or wall. Only the kitchen, a little galley in the back of the stairwell, is a defined space. It is an efficient place of production, designed much like a ship's galley. In fact, the whole house is a revelation of Beecher's dream, shorn of its dependence on the suburban myth of domesticity. Commissioned by a woman, the house dissolves the dominant orders of a male-defined propriety into the endless possibilities not of art but of daily life.

Figure 8.9: Gunta Stölzl, *Textile Design*, 1922

·163·

You can sense the same sense of liberation in the house Rudolf Schindler designed for himself and his wife and for engineer Clyde Chase and his wife in the same year in Los Angeles. Instead of creating a house for each couple, Schindler designed a spiraling concatenation of rooms that moved out through the whole lot. He sought to embrace the outside, making the captured sections of the garden into the living rooms. Outdoor fireplaces became the hearths around which the families could gather. Inside there were no bedrooms and dining rooms, but four similar spaces, each designated to one of the four par-ticipants in this living experiment. The inhabitants slept in porches on the roof. Schindler saw the house as a campground, an ephemeral encampment in the new land of California. The basic structure was a latticework of redwood woven together between slabs of concrete that had been poured on the ground and then tilted into place. Domesticity here dissolved into a campground, meeting places, and the scaffolding for the activities of everyday life.

Things did not work out that ideally. The couples soon fought, the house was divided up, and even before then it was the women who were expected to do all the cooking, albeit communally. One can see experiments like this popping up all over the world during this period. Most failed, but all shared the belief that we could reform the way we live together in this world. These experiments in modern living presented an alternative path to a society that seemed at the same time bent on destroying nature, our sense of self, and whole cultures through development, science, and war.

In one country that sense of experimentation briefly encompassed the whole society. When the Bolsheviks took over Russia in 1917, they thought they were going to build a new world. That meant not just a political change but a change of reality. The new physics of uncertainty, the disappearance of class distinctions, and the merging of public and private life all were part of the same revolution. While the feminist Aleksandra Kollontai, who was Lenin's commissar for social welfare, was proposing communal education and cooking, and while women were entering the work force alongside their comrades, artists and architects were working together in the Soviet version of the Bauhaus, the Vkhutemas (later Vkhutein). There, under the aegis of Kazimir Malevich and others, the new world was created out of teapots, uniforms, buildings, and plans. Pure color, pure form, and pure texture could transform themselves into any fragment of everyday life, from the most mundane to the most grandiose.[20]

Figure 8.10: Gerrit Rietveld, Schröder House, Utrecht, 1924

Perhaps the greatest example of this kind of thinking was Vladimir Tatlin's *Monument to the Third International* of 1920. Spiraling up to twelve hundred feet, it was a continuous line that unwrapped itself from the familiar ground and reached up to the unknown realms of a new society. Along the way it defied the rigid rules of gravity with diagonal vectors of steel that created a path of movement along which activities that would explain and spread the image of the new world would hang like jewelry off this costume of the new. The whole building was an enactment of the building of a new world. The designers had little use for the dialectics between men and women, upper and lower classes, gravity and lightness, or the man-made and the natural. Instead they wanted to construct a real alternative.

Certainly Soviet culture produced many more mundane examples of this new kind of world, including day-care centers, communal kitchens, and agricultural communes. Unfortunately the artists' and visionaries' ambitions overreached the reality of ingrained economic and sexual relations. The pressures of building a new society and the autocratic tendencies within communism itself resulted in the re-creation of the same monumental structures, excluding people rather than connecting them, that dotted the landscape of Western Europe and America. The Revolution became a style like any other. It left few tangible results in the real world other than another cycle of violence that man perpetrated on himself and the world around him.

Figure 8.11: Gerrit Rietveld, Interiors, Schröder House, Utrecht, 1924

The cantilevered mirages of liberation that jump off the pages in the work of such visionaries as Ivan Leonidov, Iakov Chernikov, and El Lissitzky still promise something new. They promise a world of revelation, where the work of construction is a continual act of breaking open and apart what is already known. Through the spiraling, curving, overlapping, and indeterminate shapes they present as notions of spaces, rather than as buildings, objects, or paintings, they allow us to glimpse the possibility of a place where we could build new relationships between ourselves and those around us.

Figure 8.12: Rudolf Schindler, Schindler/Chase House, West Hollywood, 1923

These idealistic spaces are, I believe, at the heart of that form of modernism that has its roots in an Arts and Crafts sensibility. One can find echoes of it all through the century and all around the globe, as architects experimented with new materials and forms of construction that allow us to do away with the heavy walls separating us from one another and from the world. Like Gropius, they believed that the technology out of which we create our world should be available to us in such a way that everybody could use it.

The other side of modernism was considerably less adventuresome, even if it produced more elaborate and permanent monuments to the idea of newness. The critic Beatriz Colomina has pointed out how in the work of the seminal French-Swiss architect Le Corbusier, the new world of open space, simplified to function efficiently while revealing the nature of form, somehow always managed to imprison the woman. In the photographs Le Corbusier took of the villas he designed, the woman is caught within the grids of windows and ramps or stares lovingly from the tightly packed spaces of sleeping and cooking while below her husband stands in the glorious new double-height empty space, looking out over the world, stabbing at a punching bag. All the aggressiveness and distinctions of the man-made world repeat themselves in these simplified forms.[21]

In architecture you can thus see the same movement that Picasso traced in the few years between 1911 and 1925: From the explosive reexamination of and experimentation on the spaces of everyday use that led to the labyrinths of a cubist tapestry, he retreated to the monumentalization of the female form into neoclassical, flowing, or anguished lines, hemmed in by a carefully defined space.

Figure 8.13: Vladimir Tatlin, *Monument to the Third International*, 1920

To the German thinker Walter Benjamin, it all came down to a distinction between an art of contemplation or absorption and an art of distraction. The first was the art of the Albertian window, the art that hung in the museum, the art of monumental male space. You were supposed to lose yourself in the other world that art opened up beyond the plane of the picture. It might be a new world that had learned the tricks of close-up, jump cut, and pan from film and that had unprecedented new means of representation at its disposal, but it was still an art that presented the image of an artificial world as pie in the sky available only to those who pursued the axis of progress along an abstract, violence-ridden path toward total power. Dissolving into the perfect modern spaces that began to present themselves as the stylish salons of the new in the 1920s, you would find only the latest palaces of power.

Then, said Benjamin, there was the real space of technology, specifically the brave new world of film:

By close-ups of the things around us, by focusing on hidden details of familiar objects, by exploring commonplace milieus under the ingenious guidance of the camera, the film, on the one hand, extends our comprehension of the necessities which rule our lives; on the other hand, it manages to assure us of an immense and unexpected field of action. Our taverns and our metropolitan streets, our offices and furnished rooms, our railroad stations and our factories appeared to have us locked up hopelessly. Then came the film and burst this prison-world asunder by the dynamite of the tenth of a second, so that now, in the midst of its far-flung ruins and debris, we calmly and adventurously go traveling. With the close-up, space expands; with slow motion, movement is extended. The enlargement of a snapshot does not simply render more precise what in any case was visible, though unclear: it reveals entirely new structural formations of the subject. So, too, slow motion not only presents familiar qualities of movement, but reveals in them entirely unknown ones. . . . Evidently a different nature opens itself to the camera than opens to the naked eye—if only because an unconsciously penetrated space is substituted for a space consciously explored by man. . . . The camera introduces us to unconscious optics as does psychoanalysis to unconscious impulses.[22]

Figure 8.14: Le Corbusier, Roof Terrace, Villa Savoye, Poissy, 1931

The whole world dissolved into nothing but fragments that pierced the division between self and other, inside and outside, man and woman, real and unreal. This was an art that was happening all around, a reality seen only in distraction:

Tactile appropriation is accomplished not so much by attention as by habit. As regards architecture, habit determines to a large extent even optical perception. The latter, too, occurs much less through rapt attention than by noticing the object in incidental fashion. This mode of appropriation, developed with reference to architecture, in certain circumstances acquires canonical value. For the tasks which face the human apparatus of perception at the turning points of history cannot be solved by optical means, that is, by contemplation alone. They are mastered gradually by habit under the guidance of tactile appropriation.[23]

Figure 8.15: Le Corbusier, *Living Room, Immeubles-Villas*, c. 1925

The art of distraction, that which was not consciously seen as separate from the real world but was made real by our very touch and use, was the art that would build a new world. The art of contemplation was the art of fascism that would end that new world in an orgy of self-destruction "Mankind's . . . self-alienation has reached such a degree that it can experience its self-alienation as an aesthetic pleasure of the first order."[24]

The end of the whole history of man-made building was thus either a modernism that was an inhuman style justifying a violent, ultimately self-destructive urge to transformation or the matter-of-fact construction of a new world in which the self would dissolve. These two outcomes might sound startlingly similar. Both envision the day when humanity as we have come to know it, which is, after all, a concept based on the distinction between man and woman (or principles of masculinity and femininity) and self and other, will come to an end and we will dissolve into the new universe of absolute truths and mechanization. The difference is that one is a conscious re-creation of the self, while the other will enthrone the principle of continual destruction as the center of our universe.

Neither came to pass. What we have built since then has been a world that has been more marked by uncertainty than anything else. Colomina contrasts the confident visions of Le Corbusier with the more ambiguous experiments of the Viennese architect Adolf Loos. This was the same Adolf Loos who had proposed that "ornament is crime." Loos believed that the crime lay not in the ornamentation itself but in its inappropriateness to modern ways of building. He erected a strict hierarchy that ran from the tattooed bodies of the

Figure 8.16: Pablo Picasso, *Girl with a Mandolin (Fanny Tellier)*, 1910

Hottentots to the refined simplicity of English tailoring and from the carefully crafted farmers' houses in the Alps to the clean, white, and machined surfaces of his own work. Each building, each object, and each person should have an appearance that fitted the stage of development of the society in which they made that appearance, and for modern man that meant that we no longer had to clothe ourselves in the ritualistic emblems of clan and class that had allowed us to find our way through earlier societies.[25]

Figure 8.17:
Pablo Picasso,
Two Women Running on the Beach, 1922

The shape of our current society was not one that inspired clear form of any sort. It was a complex world where the roles of men and women were uncertain. The result was a space that was always nervously on edge, as if it continually needed to redefine itself according to the shifting currents of the modern world. The outside of such houses as Loos's Müller House of 1927, for instance, is a composite of various cutoff compositions, curving and massing up without any completion in sight. On the inside the house does not flow out in uninterrupted spaces but is a concatenation of staccato half rooms that are divided from one another by partitions and half levels. All is confusion and uncertainty, as if the orders of domesticity were being stated and broken down at one and the same time. Loos's architecture is a critique of our ability to make sense of, live in, or change the orders that surround us. Instead of covering up this inability with a sheen of decoration and sublimating it under layers of the textured tools of living, or cleaning it up with the image of a new, an absolute, and a perfect solution, Loos presents us with the problem itself.

In the architecture of Adolf Loos, but also in the work of some of the other architects who were working on the margins of what we think of as modern architecture, you can no longer see male orders and female places, just as you can no longer separate the technology of construction from the reality of inhabitation. The long desire of men to create a perfect place and women to figure out a way to be at home within that framework dissolved under the onslaught of modernist thought.

Figure 8.18: Umberto Boccioni, *The Street Enters the House*, 1911

To some critics, this means that the dreams of a perfect, posthuman society modernists were presenting were becoming rooted in the reality of place and material.[26] I would argue instead that what we see in the work of especially such Nordic architects as Alvar Aalto and Gunnar Asplund is a breakdown of our belief that we can make any kind of space that represents and fixes us in a predetermined order. As the technologies of communication, education, and production make it increasingly possible for us to create more flexible personality structures, so that Dreiser's girl from a small farming community can become an actress in a big city, or an immigrant from a foreign city can reconstruct himself or herself as a member of a whole different culture, our spaces can become flexible reflections of ever-changing ways of living.

The way designers thought about what they were doing changed over the course of the century to reflect this sensibility. While at the beginning of the twentieth century the controlling metaphor was the machine, with

Figure 8.19: Adolf Loos, Ladies' Room, Müller House, Vienna, 1927

Le Corbusier dreaming of creating a "machine for living" and the futurists glorifying the victory of mechanized war, by the 1930s designers were turning to metaphors of the body. Frank Lloyd Wright, who had glorified the machine in the 1905 essay quoted in the last chapter, by the 1940s was preaching the glories of an "organic architecture," in which buildings would bloom from a central structural fact like petals of a flower. Instead of the arms that reached out to control nature from the central, phallic organized fact of the hearth in his Prairie School houses, he now proposed hexagons that would grow out in repetitive, nonhierarchical patterns. Wright designed his Usonian houses so that they would never really be finished, since the owner could keeping building additions on any of the six facets. The architecture of these houses sought to break down the distinction between order and nature, inside and outside, and the functions of separate rooms.[27]

To others, an organic architecture was more a question of appearances. Just as painters turned toward biomorphic shapes in surrealism or even brought back the monumentality of the human form, so architects began to create forms whose curves, scales, and materials echoed the human form. Aalto contrasted compacted modern rooms with splaying curves and then filled his simple rooms with plywood furniture that responded to the curve of the back and the leg. Even Le Corbusier began, after the Second World War, to create massive buildings filled with cave-like rooms that opened up into sanctuaries of light hidden deep inside forms. Their rough textures made them into monumental versions of Loos's uncertain interiors.

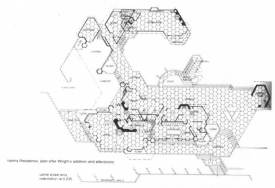

Figure 8.20: Frank Lloyd Wright, Hanna House, Palo Alto, 1936–1957

Yet even the challenge of this kind of mysterious architecture, which sought to bring humans back to an unmediated encounter with space as something that was not to be conquered but experienced in all its complexity, could be and was packaged as a style. After the Second World War, architects turned an analysis of how we move through and use space into an ever more complex pseudoscience that sought to contain "pleasure" and "texture." These became the subcategory of a system of order that was so complex that you could never see it. Just as corporate culture replaced the clarity of fascism and communism, so International Style modernism replaced the bravura gestures and complications of the earlier modernist impulses. "Architecture is almost nothing," Mies van der Rohe was famous for saying, and he created buildings, like the Seagram Building, that castrated the skyscraper and turned it into a three-dimensional piece of graph paper. His spaces were supposed to be empty enough to allow the human form to emerge, but what came out instead was mass-produced furniture that was meant to provide "the human touch" within these efficient boxes of absence.

Figure 8.21: Alvar Aalto, Lobby, Cultural Center, Wolfsburg, 1962

It turned out that architecture was at a dead end. As the critic Manfredo Tafuri has pointed out, its utopian dreams were discredited, and its pretension of being able to make concrete our ability to control all visible reality in a

Figure 8.22:
Ludwig Mies van der Rohe,
German pavilion; Georg Kolbe,
Dancer, Barcelona, 1929

centralized, hierarchical order was emptied out. The logic of this process had little to do with the dreams and architecture. It was the result of the technology of planning, the specialization in design (so that air-conditioning experts made a space comfortable, structural engineers made it stand up, and space planners figured out where everything went), and the fact that we no longer have need for a heroic architect, just as we have no more need for a heroic leader.[28] Man standing in the circle and turning it into a square has dissolved into the endless squares of apartments, office cubicles, and, eventually, computer screens.

The people who allow us to inhabit these spaces are a new breed of designers—namely, decorators or interior designers. A direct result of both the Arts and Crafts movement and the emergence of "domestic science" as a female equivalent of male science, interior design as a profession marked the entrance of women into the design world—but only in a limited arena and according to principles originally set by men. When Edith Wharton, together with Ogden Codman, Jr., wrote *The Decoration of Houses* in 1897, she carefully subjugated the placement and design of chairs, curtains, and objects of use to the architectural order, calling interior decoration no more than a "branch of architecture" that had as its function the suitable translation of function and architectural envelope into a comfortable and tasteful environment.[29]

The rules of domestic interior design were part of the same family as the rules of etiquette: They told women how to arrange their lives to reflect the male order all around them, with the elegance and grace that would make that world enjoyable.[30] Such designers as Elsie de Wolfe managed to create sumptuous yet refined interiors that elaborated on and made comfortable the stark orders of architecture. They created escapes not only from the gridded world of men but also from the logic of dissolution that threatened the spaces we inhabit.

Then a third character entered the equation. She was an African-American and of a mysterious background. She represented the unknown, the uncertain, and the exotic, offering in her actions and her very presence a critique of the dualism of the condominium and the mansion, the blond and the dark-haired. She lived in a hotel, which was like a mansion but was not a place of rooted life. Its design was postmodern—which is to say, it clothed the smooth lines and changing levels of modernism with the columns, trim, and colors of a more traditional interior.

This third character did not live there for long, but she didn't leave until she had disturbed all the simple relationships. A series of intrigues and uncertainties ensued, until everybody found his or her place again. That is what our spaces are like today. We have managed to adapt ourselves to the changing roles women and men play, to the realization of the limits of our reach to control the world, and to the changing definitions, whether scientific or philosophical, of what it means to be human, but we still inhabit the spaces of absence that we have to fill with our presence. We find ways of encapsulating the tensions, calling our ways of life postmodern and making ourselves at home by "feminizing" both modernism and traditional forms in the kinds of spaces you will see on television or in magazines. In so doing, we ironically (and sometimes self-consciously) continue to build a world in which

Figure 8.26: Krystle Carrington in Her Home, from *Dynasty*, 1983

structure, artifice, and meaning are associated with masculinity, and appearance, comfort, and reality are feminine notions. The only thing that has changed is that those of us with enough resources can afford to define where we fit within that equation.

The question remains whether we can break out of this kind of dichotomy between the made and the lived, the man-made we create and the natural we dream of, the interior and the exterior, and men and women, without papering over their differences by blurring their edges. Can we create spaces of liberation, spaces in which we can construct ourselves and our world?

9 CONSTRUCTING SEX

STARTING IN THE 1980S, women—and men—all around the United States started to experiment with ways to break through a situation in which the man-made world is made by men and women can only carve out spaces within those structures. To do this, some designers thought that they needed to create spaces that would challenge those traditional distinctions between inside and outside, between the planned and the experienced, between artificial and natural, and between useful and pleasurable that had made the cultural stereotypes of men and women into real, lived experiences. Others took a more pragmatic stance, seeking to find alternatives to the kinds of spaces that make women feel unsafe or that bind them to the traditional tasks of child rearing, cooking, and cleaning. Still others went off on a more philosophical tack, speculating on an architecture beyond building that would attack the problem at what they saw as its root—namely, the fact that we build our culture up out of a cycle of subjugation and defense and that we alienate ourselves from the world through the construction of an alternative, artificial world.

By the 1920s women were designing not just domestic interiors but stores and restaurants as well. In this country Raymond Loewy pioneered the streamlined look and arrangement of the modern department store. While men talked of the relationship between their work and the logic of production, women and retail designers developed the relationship between their work and consumption. Some designers even claimed that streamlined interiors would remove barriers to consumption and thus allow us to sail out of the Great Depression.[31] At the same time there was, as Jeffrey Meikle has pointed out, a profound ambivalence to such design:

Figure 8.23: Elsie de Wolfe, Interior, Villa Trianon, Versailles, c. 1927

> Thus the streamlined style expressed not only a phallic technological thrust into a limitless future. Its dominant image, the rounded, womblike teardrop egg, expressed also a desire for a passive, static society in which social and economic frictions engendered by technological acceleration would be eliminated. Streamlining was paradoxically a style of retreat and consolidation as well as one of penetration and forward progress.[32]

Several of the better female designers of interiors developed work that encompassed the whole world of design. Eileen Gray, a frequent collaborator with Le Corbusier, became an accomplished modernist architect in her own right. Julia Morgan, one of the few designers trained as an architect, brought a collage, a narrative, and an eclectic sensibility to buildings that were not as tightly organized as those of many of her male counterparts but were infinitely richer and more adaptable. Florence Knoll not only designed furniture that translated the cleanliness of modernism to the scale of the hand but also founded one of the most successful furniture companies in the world.

Yet these women remained isolated examples. In general, the interior and its sensibilities remained contained in the ghetto of male form. Interior design is still a profession that does not have nearly the prestige of architecture—though its practitioners often make more money—and buildings are very rarely designed from the inside out. As for the breakdown of barriers in the profession, to this day fewer than a third of the architects in this country are women.

Figure 8.24: Michael Graves,
Living Room of the Plocek Residence,
Warren, New Jersey, 1982

Not that it matters. Mainstream architecture has survived the upheavals of modernism to remain the imposition of an abstract, absolute, and inhuman order on the world. The interior remains something we all do for ourselves within those orders, only rarely hiring professionals to help us. Interiors are what we are, and we still associate them with femininity, while exteriors—appearances, buildings—are what we aspire to, and that is still a masculine order.

Postmodernism is only the latest twist in this game. It seeks to turn the making of spaces into a "language" that is a way of communicating who or what we are.[33] As such it becomes an adjunct to the clothes, objects, and food we use not because we have to but because we seek to present ourselves in a certain way. Architecture as lifestyle does not so much offer a criticism of the coldness of made spaces and the isolation of our little places as it creates a middle ground between both. Spearheaded by several homosexual male architects, it presents a way of making order more consumable and consumption more acceptable. It feminizes architecture and makes decoration and the design of the interior a more masculine pursuit. Women can dress like men, and men can be sensitive, as long as both still engage in the games of power and accept environments in which they have to create a world for themselves according to rules they don't set.

Figure 8.25: Alexis Carrington
in Her Apartment, from
Dynasty, 1983

In the 1970s the television program *Dynasty* made this situation clear.[34] In the show the evil woman had black hair, was an executive with as much power as the men, and used her body frankly. Her space was a condominium in a high-rise tower. It was modern, slick, and sleek. She was free in this space, hovering over the ground, serviced by technology. She posited the possibility of a new world where sex and power were tools anyone could use. This was not a situation accepted by mainstream society. The good woman had blond hair and lived in the mansion her husband had built. She stayed at home and took care that the grand, pillared halls and dens covered with wood grids would be filled with flowers and little knickknacks. She knew her place.

All this work is still speculative, though it is starting to construct other ways in which we can inhabit this world. This is not just a question of the intellectual desire of one group or another. Women are increasingly escaping from their traditional roles and places to the point where, in some segments of society, what men and women do and how they behave, and thus the spaces they make for themselves or how they experience spaces, are hard to tell apart. Women are gaining more political and economic power and thus demanding an end to the exclusionary practices males once did (and still) engage in. Finally the ways in which we understand our bodies and our minds have done away with most of the bases for the subjection of women to the orders of men. Out of all these changes, we must try to erect a better world.

·177·

The most pragmatic part of this work might be, at least initially, the most important. There is no question that the city is still a dangerous place for women. That is because the urban environment and its architecture are the result of centuries of oppression of violence—as well as of great beauty and achievement. As I have tried to show, that beauty and violence are intimately tied to the creation of an ever more complex world of artifice. The very attributes that make the Champs-Élysées such a beautiful place are the same qualities that make many women feel uncomfortable there, especially at night. It is a place that is all about a monumental, inhuman scale, about open spaces, and about hard surfaces. There is an intimate connection between this kind of space and the violence to which not just women but any "weak" human being finds her- or himself prone. Such grand boulevards and empty plazas are not a place of connection, conversation, or support but a testing ground for power, and only the rather thin layer of legal and moral constraints that we have spun invisibly through the city keeps that violence from living itself out. Quite often the invisible web of civility and restraint breaks down, and women are mugged, raped, beaten, or merely insulted.[1]

Figure 9.1: The Champs-Élysées on Bastille Day, Paris

The sense that the civic space of the city is a dangerous place for a woman goes back to the earliest civilization, when the woman was told she belonged inside, while the men controlled the streets. This is still true in certain Middle Eastern and even rural European societies, where women associate the road with danger.[2] What is truly frightening is that the development of a technology that demands ever more violence in its use of resources, both human and natural, has created a situation in which we all have become "feminized": We all live behind walls, whether real or electronic, in utter fear of what might happen to us if we emerged from our own little harems or oases of domesticity. The culture of fear drives a significant portion of our economy as well as our behavior. We build ever more jails as perverse mirrors of our situation of inclusion and spend ever more money keeping the streets "clean" of any mark of humanity, dirt, or violence.[3]

It is a losing proposition, because, of course, the very policing of these streets creates its own climate of violence. The perfect architecture of walls is now the invisible grid of security services, television monitors, and property laws and has become even more absolute and inhuman exactly because we cannot appropriate it through our senses.

As always, it is the weakest groups in our society, whether women or minorities, that suffer the most in this culture of fear since they do not have the means to protect themselves. All they can do is to retreat, either into the home or into the ghetto. The suburbanization of our culture, which creates ever greater distances and ever more secure and isolated places to shop, work, and learn, is only exacerbating this situation.

The answer, say many feminist critics of the city, is to create alternate models of communal living. Instead of isolated houses and empty streets, we need flexible dwellings where small groups of people can share ownership, spaces, and tasks, preferably organized around courtyards where children can play and all can feel safe. In some ways these visions do offer an alternative to the city of fear, but in other ways they merely replicate the harem.

Dolores Hayden, an architectural historian teaching at Yale, has proposed some of the most thoroughly thought-out versions of these small-scale utopias. Under her proposals of 1980 and 1984 (recently revised) a small group of women could share a suburban lot. By creating certain communal living, cooking, and even parking spaces, Hayden and her collaborators propose continuing the modernist ideal of flexible living spaces, along with the utopian dreams of communal living. These compounds would also allow for alternatives to the nuclear family, since they could expand to include an extended familial or friendship group sharing ownership, space, or identity or could be made up of individuals sharing child rearing and other tasks. What would remain would be the safe, defining environment of the compound.[4]

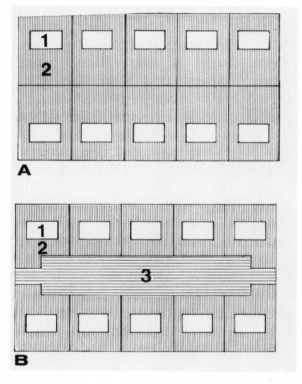

This is also its problem. The hybrid between the suburban house and the traditional community house of an earlier culture, or between the single family house and the apartment building, or between the notion of individual and collective space, can work only if it closes itself off from the outside world, repeating patterns of physical and experienced enclosure. By depending on outside technology that comes in through the invisible networks of electricity, water, and sewage, these compounds become consumers of natural resources that isolate themselves from the violence that is necessary to create such energy. By creating a perfect world inside, they restate the notion that the exterior is an alien place where we have to go and must assert ourselves to survive, while the inside is where we are safe to create our own world. The courtyard becomes the place that replaces the hearth of domesticity, where children play under the control of their mother as she cooks. Though the beauty of such compounds would be that there would be more than one "mother," and one can even imagine men taking that role, their spaces still replicate the same distinctions that continue to split our world between inside and outside, safe and violent, meaningful and powerful, and masculine and feminine.

Figure 9.2: Dolores Hayden, *Proposal for Reorganizing Suburban Lots*, 1980

·179·

Other women argue that we must just take back the streets, engaging in forceful action to wrest control of the city away from men and masculinity. Much of what critics such as Sandra Gilbert, Gerda Wekerle, and Jennifer Wolch suggest is quite logical. We indeed do not need empty plazas, gridded spaces, and grand axes. We do need streets where a variety of activities takes place night and day, where people who live there can see what is going on and thus feel a certain amount of concern for all those on the streets. We do need places where we can play, stroll, and enjoy ourselves rather than spaces that work or that are the empty results of legislation that tells us where we have to have open space.[5]

Fragments of such spaces are already coming into appearance, though they are refuges of the rich. The residential portion of Battery Park City in New York, for instance, creates a relatively small-scaled, controlled, and intimate surrounding, but it is isolated from the rest of the city by a freeway. The Miami-based designers Elizabeth Plater-Zyberk and Andres Duany have proposed communities that have the kinds of communal spaces we all would enjoy, but they are once again suburban garden city communities. The only difference is that it is likely that both father and mother will commute, leaving the children in the kibbutzlike setting of a day-care center.[6] In this way we are creating communal utopias for those who can afford them. Even in-city versions of such neighborhoods that we have wrested from single use, urban decay, and neglect by gentrification are available only to those who are well dressed enough not to be regarded as bums and told to move on.

Figure 9.3: Peter Calthorpe, *Day Care Center*, from *The Next American Metropolis*, 1993

There are two ways to see such fragments of utopian urbanism. One can see them as the building blocks for a better world that will eventually encompass the whole city, or one can see them as sublimation or prettifications of the situation that can exist only by virtue of what is around them. The houses of the rich, the day-care centers, and the stores need a supply of cheap labor that cannot afford to live in such communities. They need a great deal of disposable income. They assume that we shall all behave and that the violence that is still inherent in most sexual relations in our culture will disappear as our children grow up in these more human surroundings.

In some ways the New Traditionalism in urban planning, as this movement has come to be known, displaces the problem. Instead of men lording it over women in places where walls keep women out and men in, we have men and women retreating into their safe homes, far enough from any threat not to need more visible walls than the roving security patrol or electronic buzzer. They pay for it all by working in service-oriented jobs that remove natural resources or surplus value from many other people. The artificial world is now not just the interior but what you see on television, the protected highway, the enclosed shopping mall, the office park, and every other space where we can safely consume and produce in air-conditioned splendor. It is interesting to note, however, that children and women are the fastest-growing groups of homeless people. It is entirely possible that the very effort to create good homes for the few makes it harder for many to have any home at all and that the weakest groups in our society, women and children, are the hardest hit by this phenomenon.

If the movement toward a safer and saner city was embedded in our social and economic system, it might be a different situation. Certainly many European countries have had considerable success in creating urban environments in which all groups and both sexes can live together. In this regard Dutch urban policies seem especially enlightened. A large percentage of their governmental housing budget is reserved for the creation of spaces for single mothers, women or men living together, or other nontraditional groups. Moreover, their new housing is infill that is meant for all economic groups, and their suburban developments create communal, open, and accessible spaces as integral parts of the creation of places for people to live. There is a long tradition in the Netherlands of making do with what little space one has and seeing one's work as the remaking of that land. Today that tradition lives in the creation of such neighborhoods as the Kattenbroek area of the city of Amersfoort, where architects are experimenting with everything from the shape of houses to the curve of streets and the kinds of shopping environments to create a world that everyone can see, know, and make his or her own.

Figure 9.4: Duinker, Van Der Torre Architects, Housing at Bellamystraat 95–115, Amsterdam, 1992

One can certainly imagine, for instance, that we (the government, the community, a partnership with private developers) could take over the great monuments to consumer society, the shopping malls, and turn them into community centers. With the advent of teleshopping and the fragmentation of the market, the million-square-foot malls are becoming behemoths of the past. Yet they retain their function as perhaps the only place where people come to be together. I can easily imagine a mall in which stores were converted into offices and apartments while parking lots became parks. Already schools and community centers are setting up satellite centers in shopping malls, and this tendency could be encouraged to the point that social services and day care would also find a place there. For such a conversion to be truly successful, we would have to destroy the inward-turned design of the shopping mall by colonizing the parking lots with extra activities dotted around a park that in turn would allow the native terrain, whatever that was, to come back up through the asphalt. The great treasure chest of consumerism that once was the symbol of the feminine realm of beauty, consumption, and interiority could thus become the regenerator of a more flexible and fluid type of construction.

To create such a situation, we would need to change development policies that are completely market-driven, and we would need to have a political structure that allows for more neighborhood participation. We would also have to break through the culture of fear that keeps us all separate and that is the final sublimation of the quest for conquest that first converted the shifting boundaries of the circle around the fire into a gridded and plotted territory of exclusion.

To do this, some architects and artists argue, we must examine and work on the very notions of fear and separation themselves. We must unbuild before we construct any kind of new structure that runs the danger of becoming a monument to the dreams of one group or individual, thus keeping others out. It is no good, they say, to make great new spaces if we make them in a way that has built into them the very seeds of division. Thus any community housing or day-care center already in its very design tells people what the proper way to live in a space is, and that includes protecting traditional notions of privacy, a dependence on the washing machine and the microwave, and the use of forms that convert precious natural resources like wood into facades that stand in for us and spaces that are so flexible they are alienating. Before we build models for different modes of living, we need to take the existing structures apart to prevent the possibility that we might restart the power game in a different guise, as has happened so many times before.

To many architects working today, inspiration does not come from other architects, since the structures of exclusion, however beautiful they might be, present profound problems when you try to follow them—especially if you are a woman or a person of color. They look instead at the work of artists: the experiments in rethinking reality of El Lissitzky's "prouns"; the cubist mixture of person and object, man and woman, interior and exterior; the profound questioning of the relationship between sexuality and production, viewing and using, naming and experiencing in the work of Marcel Duchamp; the collage sensibilities of *arte povera*; the opening up of the built environment in the work of Gordon Matta-Clark.

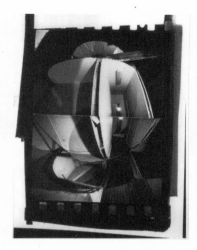

Figure 9.5: Gordon Matta-Clark, *Caribbean Orange Series*, 1978

The work of the latter artist is of special interest to me because it is all about the breaking open of the barriers that separate inside from outside. In the process Matta-Clark first creates a surreal juxtaposition between the normal rituals of domesticity and the world of the city, so that you can imagine stepping from the dresser not to the bed, in works such as the 1975 *Conical Intersect* or the 1978 *Circus,* but into the street in your nightgown. What is private is on display, and what is public continues from the private. There is no sense of shelter and appearance, only the spiraling connection between a small object or texture and the grand facades of the city.

What allows this profound sense of connection to exist is a violence he does to the structures of oppression. This was, of course, a standard revolutionary tactic, wholly proper to the 1960s. Like a good rock 'n' roller or Che-ist, Matta-Clark took his Sawzall and swung it at the all-too-visible structures of oppression and, as a result, opened up a space of liberation. Beyond such bravura, however, there is another dimension to this work. Stepping into his work is like falling into Alice's hole, since you find yourself spiraling into a world where the normal relations of things have been replaced not by something else but by their own reversal: What was in is now out; what was solid is now void; what was the space of women is now the space of men. Unlike some other artists, Matta-Clark does not stop there. His constructions give back something else: a circle, an oblong and attenuated ellipse, or a splayed crack that presents a real alternative to the orthogonal prisons all around us. It is a world that you cannot inhabit—it is, after all, just a void—but it is a very real cut in the real world that reorganizes everything around it. Finally, the work of Matta-Clark is ephemeral. It exists today only in photographs and a few rather sad leftover fragments. If it were to have lasted, preserved behind ropes and treated like an artwork to be seen in contemplation, it would have become just another form of monument. As it is, it remains as an active critique, existing only in memory and in a few images.[7]

Matta-Clark had a profound influence on the architect who has most challenged the structures of sexual and social oppression within the profession itself, Frank Gehry. This architect's own house, designed in 1979, is a case study in how a building can be "Matta-Clarked" and then inhabited.

Gehry designed an addition to the house that is neither another pavilion of domestic delight nor a seamless extension of the traditional order of the house, but a wrapper that elides eating, cooking, and playing into an L-shaped geometry that is difficult to define as a separate space. To increase the confusion, Gehry paved the floor with asphalt, as if this were just a driveway that somehow had become enclosed. The new space is lower than the existing *piano nobile* of the house, so that a Loosian nervousness about the proper place and boundary of all the rituals of domesticity sets in. The window over the kitchen area is a riff on El Lissitzky's *Proun 99*, a tumbling fragment of geometry that cuts through the straight up-and-down construction to promise at least a little piece of utopia.

Figure 9.6: Frank Gehry, Kitchen, Gehry Residence, Santa Monica, 1978

Not content merely to add these possibilities, Gehry ripped away at the existing building, exposing wood stud walls and rafters, leaving windows hanging in their frames on a sea of old studs, and replacing the wood siding in front of the master bed upstairs with glass. You get a glimpse of the construction of a little domestic world, complete with a chimney and the peak of the roof, so that the whole resembles a kid's drawing of a house. The exposed construction of the house serves several functions. It reveals the history of the house, so that the new construction does not so much impose a new order as it reveals and examines an already existing one. It revels in the process of construction, so that the process of making, seeing, and knowing replaces the consumption of what has been made for you. Finally it creates a tapestry of shapes that surround you and weave space together into places of both gathering and connection. You are never quite inside or outside, controlled by architecture or free from it, or even certain where in the process of (re)construction you are at the moment. By looking around you, exploring with your eye or your hand or your body, you can find your way through a material world.

Figure 9.7: Frank Gehry, Kitchen Window, Gehry Residence, Santa Monica, 1978

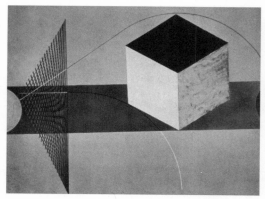

Figure 9.8: El Lissitzky,
Proun 99, 1925

In his later architecture Gehry has continued to be concerned with a breakdown in the process by which we create monuments that constrain us by telling us where to go, what to do, or what is meaningful. His symbol is the fish—a slippery, asexual, yet sexually evocative thing, a smelly and fishy shape that is not architecture, not human, and not constructed. Yet it somehow manages to stand for our own sublimated desires and fears, for beauty itself, and for a desire not to engage in the games of power. While many of his buildings cannot escape from such games and end up by turning into monuments whose slippery qualities are perhaps aestheticized to the point where they fulfill the role of a revolutionary painting hung in a museum, the impulse to unmake and create a slippage in how we live remains.

One could follow the implications of Gehry's architecture of the period when he designed his house to a logical extreme and imagine a world in which housing was only a scaffolding, made out of mass-produced elements, onto which we could clip the activities of everyday life. This tapestry of construction could become a web or shifting layering of screens that would continually reveal its own making. It would leave us free to construct our own roles. Instead of male architects' creating abstract orders and female inhabitants' creating places within those orders, we would have a continuum of construction, experience, and architectural experimentation.

To a younger generation of architects, such a world is possible only if you avoid Gehry's more conventional construction practices. As soon as you have a client, a program, and a site, you are stuck; you have to create productive, efficient spaces that reproduce standard social relations. Instead, these designers suggest, architecture is something we should continually stage.

Figure 9.9: Frank Gehry,
Bathroom Window,
Gehry Residence,
Santa Monica, 1978

New York architects Elizabeth Diller and Ricardo Scofidio did this with a series of projects in the late 1980s, including *The Rotary Notary and His Hot Plate*, a 1987 performance at New York's La Mama Theater. In it they turned

Marcel Duchamp's 1912–1923 *Large Glass (The Bride Stripped Bare by her Bachelors, Even)* into a space. The stage, a metal frame, and mirrors turned the window/mirror of Duchamp's piece (which had itself been a comment on the relationship between the notions of an ideal projected through a window and the mirror of reality) into an occupiable space—if only for the inhabitants. The actors took the place of the various fragments of instruments and shadows of pollution that made up the "subject" in the original. The work of the architects here involved restaging the original relations so that the bride is no longer stripped bare. Her supine position becomes a vertical one, and she takes the place of the Vitruvian man squaring the circle, except that no complete geometry results. We are left in a state of suspended spatial animation.[8]

Such suspension continued in Diller/Scofidio's installation at the Capp Street Project in San Francisco, where a dining table and chairs were hung from the ceiling, so that the ritual of family dining was displaced to a plane where it could no longer function. They also cut open the wall to the outside in line with a rift in the floor and placed a chair, cut down the middle, in front of this

Figure 9.10: Frank Gehry, *Fish Lamp*, 1983

hole. Thus a Matta-Clarkian strategy of cutting created a manner of peephole in reverse: The outside world now became the thing you looked at, except that you could never quite get comfortable in your viewing position.

Notions of "specularity" and "the scopic regime" figure prominently in such work. To many critics, "the male gaze" is the very instrument of oppression, and the work of a truly feminist artist would be to refuse to lie down in front of that gaze or to mimic it by standing up to the man. Instead they should replace it with a textual or contextual weaving that frustrates viewing itself, mirrors it, or replaces it with a system of haptic, or felt, sense.[9] For architects, this often means appropriating the methods of surveillance and control and turning them back on themselves, as Diller/Scofidio did in 1990 in an installation in the very temple of specularity, the Museum of Modern Art in New York. There they connected security cameras, placed at moments of entrance and movement between floors, to monitors placed in front of chairs again hung from the ceiling, so that they were unreachable.

Such work might seem abstract and even absurd, but it does try to attack exactly the notion that we create structures only to make things clearer. By subjecting ourselves to the idea that buildings should keep certain things out, should be comfortable, and should affirm our expectations about space, these architectural experimenters are saying, we are giving in to a situation in which we will continue to associate, on the one hand, action, outside, production, and men, and, on the other, contemplation, comfort, inside, reproduction, and women. The architect John Whiteman attacked this notion directly with a small pavilion he designed in 1989 in Austria. It was no more than a scaffolding with no floor, so you were not even sure it was a building or a space. You could move it only by pivoting the various portions of the walls. These were burnished metal plates that could move precisely because they had proportions that Whiteman derived from the measurements that a standard handbook for architects, *Architectural Graphic Standards*, gives for men and women. You slipped in and out of a space that was not quite a defined place by manipulating the supposed differences between the sexes.

The architect Peter Eisenman has made a career out of trying to deny authorship and male power (while using it to great effect). He thus hopes to open up an uncertain space of multiple readings that slip away from the tyranny of the known. In 1993 he proposed a building for the Max Reinhardt Institute in Berlin that he said was "male-female." He derived its DNA-like form from a computer program that generated differential equations. The building was to spiral up into the sky like a phallic skyscraper, though twisting and turning in ways that frustrated any attempt to read it as a singular object. Then its U shape should cause it to return to the ground. This rather cartoonlike castration of the skyscraper will never be built, but it

Figure 9.13: Elizabeth Diller and Ricardo Scofidio, *Para-site,* 1990

does present a strong example of one of the most important current trends in critical architecture: the notion that we can slip out of the dichotomies of sex by entering the realm of uncertainty, chaos, strange attractors, and computer programs opened up by quantum physics and other advances in the sciences.

This mechanism of production connects directly to attempts to see the whole world as woven together out of the fragments of sense and sensuality that predate spoken and written language, thus trying to undo the importance we give not only to intelligible words but to the narratives we construct out of them. This is an effort now known as deconstructivism and based on the work of the French critic Jacques Derrida. It has yet to produce, however, any examples of architectural experimentation that create the kind of tapestry of previsual and prenarrative or nomadic order of which its practitioners dream.[10]

Figure 9.14: John Whiteman, *Divisible by 2,* St. Pölten, 1988

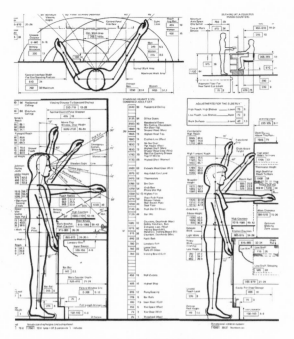

Figure 9.15: *Anthropometric Standards for Workstations*

Perhaps this is because, as some of them claim, such a construction is by definition impossible; to build is to create inside and outside. Just by the act of differentiation and coordination involved with any act of construction, you will produce an object that will be owned and that will reproduce existing social relations. Instead some avant-garde designers propose spaces that are "free" or "open" and can only exist in dreams themselves. The Viennese firm Coop Himmelblau has long claimed that it escapes the hierarchies of the modern world by drawing "psychograms." These are preconscious doodles the designers construct with their eyes closed. They then build these sketches literally, or so they claim. Out of the unconscious comes a flowing insertion into the world that breaks through expectations, use, and stable construction to create "a space of the open mind, the open heart, open space."[11]

Such an open space is also the goal of the New York architect Lebbeus Woods, who dreams of creating "freespaces" made up of cooperative communities that are engaged in a kind of high tech Arts and Crafts: They are continually making and remaking a communal world whose only function is to make itself. It is a world that exists floating in the sky or burrowing underground. It might even become a fragment that clamps on to buildings, but it never completes itself. It is building, not a building.[12] Yet even Woods, who claims that he does want to build, worries about the implications of his work. In his recent *Architecture and War* series, he draws frighteningly aggressive metallic shapes that might be machines or monsters, cranes or tanks, constructive or destructive. All architecture, he seems to be saying, is an act of violence. It uses up resources, replaces place with territory, creates insides and outsides and hierarchies. You cannot avoid it. You might as well draw it, draw it out, and face it.[13]

Figure 9.16: Peter Eisenman, Max Reinhardt Institute, Berlin, 1993

·190·

In a sense the only way architecture would seem to be able to avoid this predicament is to stop becoming an autonomous activity. To some theorists and architects, the work of building should realize its prosthetic nature: You should not create freestanding buildings and new spaces (and thus hierarchies) but should replace and extend your body through a melding with the technology of transformation and appropriation. Our clothes, our machines, and our buildings all are extensions of ourselves into the world. They are how we appear and make the world our own. They are also how we internalize the world, since they allow us to understand and survive in the world. The spaces we make to house this continual activity of interiorization and exteriorization

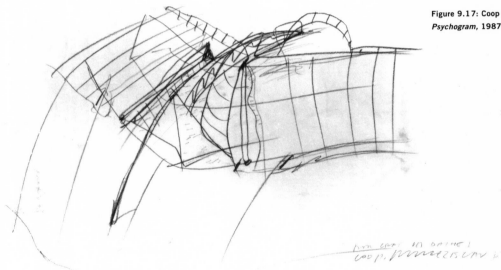

Figure 9.17: Coop Himmelblau, *Psychogram*, 1987

are the problem. They limit what we can do and what we can understand. When you are in a house, you are no longer able to do what you want but must follow certain rules.

What if, instead, architecture was that which continually broke open, measured, interpreted, and allowed you to remain within a world you were creating? What if it was a device that allowed you to connect with the world, rather than make a world separate from the reality? What if architecture was not a building but a making, an experiment on and in the real world?[14]

Figure 9.18: Lebbeus Woods, *Aerial Paris*, 1989

Figure 9.19: Lebbeus Woods, *Underground Berlin*, 1988

Such an activity might sound farfetched, but it is central to what some feminist theorists are posing as the possibility of living beyond the prisons of sex and gender. Central to their efforts is the belief that we cannot remain caught in a condition in which masculinity and femininity, or man and woman, are just names for two poles in a play of power. We have elaborated the original differentiation between ourselves and the world, and between the self and the world, that allows us to make ourselves into human beings and into a system of hierarchies in which the self has become a defensive bastion. We define our insides as what matters and our appearances as that which we present as a system of external coherence in order to present and defend those insides. As

Simone de Beauvoir has pointed out, men articulate this effort externally, women internally.[15] Men extend their work into the conquest of territory; women retreat into the making of a self inside. Whether this bifurcation has any relationship to biological fact matters little, as both are versions of the same distinction between inside and outside.

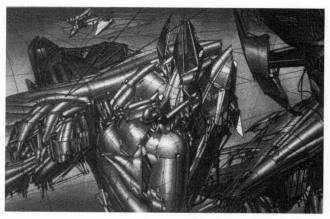

Figure 9.20: Lebbeus Woods, *Architecture and War*, 1992

A historical process that has led to the subjugation of the inward-turned strategy to the external one has only exacerbated the situation. We have chosen, as a culture, the path of rationality, progress, and the desire to make ourselves real in the world by building versions of ourselves, rather than by internalizing the world and finding ways of weaving connections to what appears around us. Neither strategy would avoid the plays of power, since both privilege certain aspects of the world as we act on it, and both disconnect us from the world at the same time as these theories attempt to create connections to it. Whether we create an alternate world turned inward around the campfire or move out to build a brave new world on ever-receding far horizons, we still are creating an artifice that subjects us to the continual question of what is real, what matters, and how and by whom decisions are made.

Thus it is not a question of "ecofeminism," as some have argued.[16] We cannot pretend that we can "use" the world in a more responsible way by renouncing violence, hierarchy, meat eating, and waste. We will still create structures of difference; we will still live in a consuming culture that operates by constructing complicated relationships based on what we make, what we use, and who owns those products. Not to do so would be not to be human—an idea that appeals only to the most radical ecofeminist. Just because a woman gives birth and nurses does not make her more caring or nurturing. It just means that her fantasy about the world, that which allows her to make sense out of the world, is made up of dreams of reproduction, connection, and interiorization, rather than of production, territory, and externalization.

Figure 9.21: Cyborg, from *Aliens*, 1986

Perhaps we need, as Donna Haraway has suggested, to think of a third kind of being, one that is neither masculine nor feminine: a cyborg. As she puts it, "I would rather be a cyborg than a goddess."[17] This cyborg is an organism that is both a body and a human being, and neither. It is the condensation of a universe of prosthetics made up of tools, cars, air conditioning, and buildings that replace our body's functions. In that system we are all conscious nodes in a continuous network that you might see as our ecosystem, the universe of information, or our society. What we think of as individuals are only sedimentations of information, flesh, opinions, clothes. They are ways we are seen and see others:

> In so far as we know ourselves in both formal discourse (for example, biology) and in daily practice (for example, the homework economy in the integrated circuit), we find ourselves to be cyborgs, hybrids, mosaics, chimeras. Biological organisms have become biotic systems, communications devices like others. There is no fundamental, ontological separation in our formal knowledge of machine and organism, of technical and organic.[18]

We change and develop together with the world around us, remaining a point of perspective, a particular glance askew at the structures all around us. There is nothing stable or permanent about us. All that is real, says Haraway, is the continual construction of what we call our self.[19]

All she asks us is to delight in being that "cyborg":

> A cyborg is a cybernetic organism, a hybrid of machine and organism, a creature of social reality as well as a creature of fiction. . . . By the late twentieth century, our time, a mythic time, we are all chimeras, theorized and fabricated hybrids of machines and organisms; in short, we are cyborgs. . . . The cyborg does not dream of community on the model of the organic family, this time without the oedipal project. The cyborg would not recognize the Garden of Eden; it is not made of mud and cannot dream of returning to dust. Perhaps that is why I want to see if cyborgs can subvert the apocalypse of returning to nuclear dust in the manic compulsion to name the Enemy. Cyborgs are not reverent; they do not re-member the cosmos. They are wary of holism, but needy for connection.[20]

Traditionally, says Haraway, we as a culture have concerned ourselves with boundaries and thresholds: What makes mine and yours, what is my body and what is not, what is the amount of chromosomes or testosterone necessary to make a man or a woman. Instead, she says, we should be interested in "boundary crossings," "splittings," and networks:

> If it was ever possible ideologically to characterize women's lives by the distinction of public and private domains—suggested by images of the division of working-class life into factory and home, of bourgeois life into market and home, and of gender existence into personal and political realms—it is now a totally misleading ideology, even to show how both terms of these dichotomies construct each other in practice and theory. I prefer a network ideological image, suggesting the profusion of spaces and identities and the permeability of boundaries in the personal body and in the body politic. "Networking" is both a feminist practice and a multinational corporate strategy—weaving is for oppositional cyborgs.[21]

Her model of what defines self is not appearance or mechanism but immune system: "Immunity can also be conceived in terms of shared specificities; of the semipermeable self able to engage with others (human and nonhuman, inner and outer), but always with finite consequences; of situated possibilities and impossibilities of individuation and identification; and of partial fusions and dangers."[22]

Out of this Haraway arrives at a "feminist theory":

> Perhaps, ironically, we can learn from our fusions with animals and machines how not to be Man, the embodiment of Western logos. From the point of view of pleasure in these potent and taboo infusions, made inevitable by the social relations of science and technology, there might indeed be a feminist science. . . . That is why cyborg politics insists on noise and advocates pollution, rejoicing in the illegitimate fusions of animal and machine. These are the couplings which make Man and Woman so problematic, subverting the structure of desire, the force imagined to generate language and gender, and so subverting the structure and modes of reproduction of "Western" identity, of nature and culture, of mirror and eye, slave and master, body and mind.[23]

Such a fluid definition of self is shared, in a perhaps more romantic way, by the French philosopher Luce Irigaray. Irigaray is convinced that we have constructed "the male" as time and "the woman" as place. "Woman" is what we call that from which we emerge. It is the name that we give to our location in space. It is the womb, the origin, nature. "Man" is what we call action, the changes that transform that space into an evolving entity:

> As man re-creates woman from outside, from inside-outside, he re-places himself outside, as an actor outside, a creator outside. By actively putting himself outside, he re-sculpts a body for himself. By using a tool? He reconstructs his own body as a result of engendering the body of the other. By using his hand, his penis—which is not merely a tool of pleasure, but a truly useful tool of alliance, incarnation, creation. Woman, insofar as she is a container, is never a closed one. Place is never closed. The boundaries touch against one another while still remaining open.[24]

Irigaray then asks us to imagine how we can use these very images to open up communication and relationship between man and woman. She uses the traditional image of the woman who is the possessor of veils, standing watch over the threshold of her house or body:

> Beneath her veils, she keeps secret watch over a threshold. A slight opening onto the depths or abysses of all languages, birth, and generation. It is up to the male lover to find there or to perceive the fall into amorphousness or the astonishment of what has not yet been given form or revealed from above. To bring about with her, and through or in spite of her, the assumption of the flesh. . . .[25]

It is thus not a question of dissolving into a mechanical universe, or discovering that one is something else, but of opening up another space within our culture. Irigaray proposes a "vegetal blossoming" that could come from woman's confidence in space, but this is not a force of pure femininity. It is rather a movement, through porous layers and veils, toward a communal desire that will allow one to explore the space of fantasy out of which one can construct one's self as a carnal being. We require a new conception of space-time for this, and Irigaray imagines that we need architects to build such a new world:

> Architects are needed. Architects of beauty who fashion *jouissance* [joy]—a very subtle material. Letting it be and building with it, while respecting the approach, the threshold, the intensity. Urging it to unfold without a show of force. Only an accompaniment? It only unfolds itself from being unfolded. It is in touch with itself from being touched while touching itself. It must be able to inhere. To continue to live in itself in order to live with. One must reach the heart of one's habitation in order to cohabit. This heart is always in motion and, at the same time, does not lack a dwelling. A qualitative threshold makes it possible for love to endure.[26]

This world of love is not a world of romance, nor is it a world of melting bodies. It is a world in which we come to a fundamentally different understanding of ourselves, whether as women, men, or beings, united only in desire and in the fantastical artifices we communally create out of that.

This is perhaps an abstract effort. It is up to more radical feminists such as Judith Butler to propose the political dimensions of these activities. Butler does not believe that sex is a given. Instead she believes that our "sexuality" is a materialization over time of the identity that we must live in order to operate in society. We become the physical manifestations of our social relations. That identity is what allows us to be social humans. She resists current divisions between sex and gender that would make the first innate and the second a social attribute because she believes that division already privileges one over the other: Sex is the "base," natural and most often feminine, while "gender" is the fancy construct we make, that which is gendered, as in that which differentiates itself and is most often male.[27] Instead she proposes that we are real as sexual beings in a way that involves behavior, body, politics, and identity. This organism's prime characteristic is that it works or that it comes into being as a "regulatory ideal" that makes us function:

In this sense, then, "sex" not only functions as a norm, but is part of a regulatory practice that produces the bodies it governs, that is, whose regulatory force is made clear as a kind of productive power, the power to produce—demarcate, circulate, differentiate—the bodies it controls. Thus "sex" is a regulatory ideal whose materialization is compelled, and this materialization takes place (or fails to take place) through certain highly regulated practices. In other words, "sex" is an ideal construct which is forcibly materialized through time. It is not a simple fact or static condition of the body, but a process whereby regulatory norms materialize "sex" and achieve this materialization through a forcible reiteration of those norms. That this reiteration is necessary is a sign that materialization is never complete, that bodies never quite comply with the norms by which their materialization is impelled. "Sex" is, thus, not simply what one has, or a static description of what one is: it will be one of the norms by which the "one" becomes viable at all, that which qualifies the body for life within the domain of cultural intelligibility.[28]

This process involves the creation of what Butler calls "abjection." The self defines itself by its power over another, as not-the-other and that which defines the other.[29] It does so by "citing" and "siting" power. This is the crux of how we use sex to run our society.[30] Butler points out that power is always located in our ability to identify ourselves or something in our control with something absent. We cite the law, the God, precedent, natural facts, or some other absent fact that defines what a thing is. If somebody opposes us, we can cite the law in our defense, or our God-given right. We can also site power: We can take up arms, create a territory in which and through which we articulate our power. We can define ourselves through what is absent and what we make present through citing and siting.

These are the powers that I have identified throughout this book with what we think of as male in our society. The artificial creation of a separate world that operates through abstract mechanism makes for a world marked as male in language, act, and deed. You cannot oppose such a world by retreat into an imagined femininity that will connect one to the world. You can start instead by offering an alternative to such an operation by citing other forms of human culture and siting them at the campfire, but this is not enough. We must realize that such constructions already exist in the male universe.

Instead we can reimagine ourselves as cyborgs, relational networks, veiled thresholds of desire, and architects of *jouissance,* or pleasure. Whatever we do, we must construct ourselves first and foremost in the here and now. We must site and cite ourselves as ourselves—which is to say, as artificial beings that create their own world but only in relationship to others. Our brave new world is one that we have to build together. The means to do this are indirect and slippery. They avoid dualism and the plays of power because, as Butler points out, cracks always open up in the construction of the self: "Indeed, it is the instabilities, the possibilities for rematerialization, opened up by this process that mark one domain in which the force of the regulatory law can be turned against itself to spawn rearticulations that call into question the hegemonic force of that very regulatory law."[31]

If we are no more or less than materialization of social conditions that have imprisoned us in sexual and social roles, then the very weight and complexity of that sedimentation by its very nature open up pockets, fissures, and other inconsistencies in the construction of ourselves. We are, after all, real human beings that have to live out our lives in unpredictable ways that allow doubt, or "the other," or if nothing else, a world that is not just what we contain within our bodies or minds to seep in.

Such a space of doubt, located in the construction of ourselves, might be labeled a "queer space." The name comes from "queer theory," an effort to theorize homosexual identity. Butler herself argues for "queering" identity, and for the construction of undecidable genders that "pass" from male to female or allow us to pass as either. That is the aim of her book: to argue for the construction of a queer identity that escapes from the plays of power.

Figure 9.22: Rosanna Liebman, *Porch*, 1994

Yet we can think of queer space as something different. It is a space of difference, where one realizes that desire is not biological destiny, and neither is our social role. It is a doubt about the citing of gender in sex. It is a doubt about our identity. In this form of self-criticism, in this possibility of another fantasy, lies the possibility of liberation. It is a queer space, an odd space, one that has no particular shape or site, but one that continually slips into the activities of everyday life, transforming them into a fantastical world of possible desire.

What would such a space look like? It would not be the proud erection of complete and monumental objects. It would not be a tapestry of connection woven out of and through the world. It would be ourselves dissolving into the communal construction of an always changing world. It would be a criticism of the world we make that seeps into the very act of making. It would be an experimental architecture, a sexy seduction into possible, dangerous, delightful worlds. It would be a free space in which we can construct ourselves together.

I do not know what such a space will look like. I do know that it will not be a sited space or a building. We do not need more buildings. We need an architecture of liberation that allows us all to re-create fantastically the world we have already made and make it our own. I think of this space as a kind of porch. It is part of a house but is also outside. There is an order there but not one of halls. In a good porch the wood or steel all around you creates a web from which you can hang, through which you can see, or in which you can sit. It is permeable. Screens filter the world; forms are implied; the body is implicated; things make sense.

I am sitting on that porch, looking out through a world that is defined by columns, a balustrade, an awning. The wood of the porch is constructed, and I can see how it was made, how it could be remade. There is a breeze, a sound of someone's entering and joining this space with me. I am swinging on a chair. I imagine how the world around me could keep going, but I also feel the world seeping in. This is a real place, a place that could unconstruct our buildings. It is a place of veils, scrims, of being in between. I imagine making love on this porch.

Notes

Chapter 1: Of Penises and Tents

1. Erik E. Erikson, "Inner and Outer Space: Reflections on Womanhood," reprinted by permission of *Daedalus,* Journal of the American Academy of Arts and Sciences, from the issue entitled "The Woman in America," Spring 1964, Volume 93, Number 2.

2. Ibid., p.587.

3. The feminist critique of Freudianism has by now become almost as powerful as the traditional male-dominated doctrine. Perhaps the most coherent exponent of this critique in relation to the way in which spatialization takes place is Nancy Chodorow (Nancy Chodorow, *The Reproduction of Mothering: Psychoanalysis and the Sociology of Gender* [Berkeley: University of California Press, 1978]), though again she accepts the "natural" development of different modes of spatial orientation, even while pointing out the social dimensions of such emerging sensibilities.

4. Martin Luther, "The Difference Between Men and Women; Table Talk #55," *Luther's Works,* Vol. 54, ed. and tr. Theodore G. Toppert (Philadelphia: Fortress Press, 1967), p. 8.

5. Camille Paglia, *Sexual Personae: Art and Decadence from Nefertiti to Emily Dickinson* (New York: Vintage Books, 1991 [1990]).

6. This issue is discussed more fully in Chapter 2. See also Ann Bergren, "Architecture Gender Philosophy," in *Strategies of Architectural Thinking,* ed. John Whiteman, Jeffrey Kipnis, and Richard Burdett (Chicago: Chicago Institute for Architecture and Urbanism, 1992), pp. 8–46, and Marilyn B. Arthur, "The Dream of a World Without Women: Poetics and the Circles of Order in the *Theogony* Prooemium," *Arethusa,* Vol. 16, no. 1–2 (1983), pp. 97–116.

7. It is difficult to pin down the source of this commonplace in college literature courses, but it probably dates to the post–World War II popularity of the works of C. S. Lewis and Erich Fromm.

8. Simone de Beauvoir, *The Second Sex,* tr. and ed. H. M. Parshley (New York: Vintage Books, 1989 [1949]), p. 36.

9. Ibid., p. 3.

10. Donna J. Haraway, *Simians, Cyborgs, and Women: The Reinvention of Nature* (New York: Routledge, 1991): "Without question, the modern evolutionary concept of a population, as the fundamental natural group, owes much to classical ideas of the body politic, which in turn are inextricably interwoven with the social relationships of production and reproduction" (p. 7).

11. Ibid., p. 40.

12. A summary of such arguments can be found in Gerda Lerner, *The Creation of Patriarchy* (New York, Oxford University Press, 1986), p. 18ff, esp. p. 43: "[Elise] Boulding sees in the Neolithic societies an egalitarian sharing of work, in which each sex developed appropriate skills and knowledge essential for group survival. She tells us that food gathering demanded elaborate knowledge of the ecology, of plants and trees and roots, their properties as food and as medicine. She describes primitive woman as guardian of the domestic fire, as the inventor of clay and woven vessels, by means of which the tribe's surpluses could be saved for lean times. She describes woman as having elicited from plants and trees and fruits the secrets of transforming their products into healing substances, into dyes and hemp and yarn and clothing. Woman knew how to transform the raw materials and dead animals into nurturing products. Her skills must have been as manifold as those of man and certainly as essential. Her knowledge was perhaps greater [than] or at least as great as his; it is easy to imagine that it would have seemed to her quite sufficient. In the development of ritual and rites, of music and dance and poetry, she had as much of a part as he did. And yet she must have known herself responsible or life-giving and nurturance. Woman, in precivilized society, must have been man's equal and may well have felt herself to be his superior."

13. Cf. Elise Boulding, *The Underside of History: A View of Women Through Time* (Boulder, Colo.: Westview Press, 1976), p. 10ff.

14. Claude Lévi-Strauss, *The Elementary Structures of Kinship*, tr. James Harle Bell and John Richard von Sturmer (Boston: Beacon Press, 1969).

15. Gottfried Semper, "Style in the Technical and Tectonic Arts or Practical Aesthetics. A Handbook for Technicians, Artists, and Patrons of Art" (1860), *The Four Elements of Architecture and Other Writings*, tr. Harry Francis Mallgrave and Wolfgang Herrman (Cambridge, England: Cambridge University Press, 1989), pp. 181–263, 254.

16. The most moving discussion of nomad culture can be found in Bruce Chatwin's *The Songlines* (New York: Vintage Books, 1987). Chatwin argues that our nomadic past continues to haunt our culture, destabilizing those structures of permanence that try to repress it. Gilles Deleuze and Félix Guattari, in their *A Thousand Plateaus: Capitalism and Schizophrenia*, tr. Brian Massumi (Minneapolis: University of Minnesota Press, 1987), place such musings in a more sweeping setting by seeing "the nomadic war machine" as a force that enters into sedentary agricultural settlements, introduces such new technologies as horse riding to those cultures, and thus allows for a differentiation of social and spatial territories.

17. Cf. Torvald Faegre, *Tents: Architecture of the Nomads* (Garden City, N.Y.: Anchor Books, 1979).

18. Elizabeth Weatherford, "Women's Traditional Architecture," *Heresies: A Feminist Publication on Art and Politics*, Issue 2: "Patterns of Communication and the Use of Space," May 1977, p. 35.

19. Abbé Laugier, *Essai sur l'Architecture* (Paris: 1775). This text had become central to much architectural theory and has only fairly recently come under critical observation for its unfounded assumptions. See especially Joseph Rykwert, *On Adam's House in Paradise: The Idea of the Primitive Hut in Architectural Theory* (Cambridge, Mass.: MIT Press, 1981), pp. 43–50.

20. Rykwert, p. 44.

21. Cf. Deborah Cameron, *Feminism and Linguistic Theory* (London: Macmillan Publishers, 1985); Robin Tolmach Lakoff, *Language and Woman's Place* (New York: Harper & Row, 1989); Casey Miller, *Words and Women* (Garden City, N.Y.: Anchor Books, 1977).

22. Jacques Derrida, "Plato's Pharmacy," *Disseminations*, tr. Barbara Johnson (Chicago: University of Chicago Press, 1981 [1972]), pp. 61–172.

23. For a good collection of such arguments, see Gisela Ecker, ed., *Feminist Aesthetics*, tr. Harriet Anderson (Boston: Beacon Press, 1986).

24. John Dewey, *Art as Experience* (New York: Perigee Books, 1980 [1934]), p. 34.

25. Daphne Spain, in *Gendered Spaces* (Chapel Hill: University of North Carolina Press, 1992), points out that anthropological studies show "controlled intimacy" in nomadic tents that divides them into two sides, often with distinctly different qualities. In Berber tents the south side is light, male, higher, the place of entrance, and associated with culture, while the north is female, dark, and associated with nature (p. 37). Even among Navajos, where women have more power than men in religion and kinship, the hogan is the man's place, with a "female" floor and "male" sky held up by poles, but they are seen as complementary, not hierarchical. Thus segregation doesn't necessarily lead to lower status for women (p. 59), though where there is no segregation, women have the greatest kinship power. "Societies in which gender stratification is most pronounced are also those in which men have the most knowledge to protect. The geographic segregation created by men's huts helps accomplish that goal, and in turn it reinforces and reproduces status differences between women and men" (p. 79).

26. Charlotte Perkins Gilman, *The Man-Made World or Our Androcentric Culture* (New York: Charlton Company, 1911), pp. 37–41.

27. Lewis Mumford, Excerpts from *The City in History: Its Origin, Its Transformation, and Its Prospects,* copyright ©1961 and renewed 1989 by Lewis Mumford; reprinted by permission of Harcourt Brace & Company, p. 89.

Chapter 2: Spaces of Domination, Tricks of Domesticity

1. Much history of the cultures of Mesopotamia remains speculative, but the strength of male domination can be clearly read in the many myths in which goddesses are replaced by war gods. For a summary of recent scholarship in this area, see Anne Baring and Jules Cashford, *The Myth of the Goddess: Evolution of an Image* (New York: Penguin Books, 1993), esp. p. 158ff.

2. Lewis Mumford, Excerpts from *The City in History: Its Origin, Its Transformation, and Its Prospects,* copyright ©1961 and renewed 1989 by Lewis Mumford; reprinted by permission of Harcourt Brace & Company, p. 27.

3. Baring and Cashford, p. 175ff.

4. Elise Boulding, *The Underside of History: A View of Women Through Time* (Boulder, Colo.: Westview Press, 1976), p. 124ff; Gabriele Geiger, *Frauen, Körper, Bauten: Weibliche Wahrnehmung des Raums am Beispiel Stadt* (München: Profil Verlag, 1986), p. 44.

5. Geiger, p. 47.

6. This concept is central especially to Gilles Deleuze and Félix Guattari, *A Thousand Plateaus: Capitalism and Schizophrenia,* tr. Brian Massumi (Minneapolis: University of Minnesota Press, 1987).

7. Karl Marx, *Capital: A Critique of Political Economy,* tr. Samuel Moore and Edward Aveling (New York: Modern Library, n.d. [1867]), p. 786ff.

8. Friedrich Engels, *The Origins of the Family, Private Property and the State,* quoted in Gerda Lerner, *The Creation of Patriarchy* (New York, Oxford University Press, 1986), p. 23.

9. One prevalent theory is that "The most likely reason for female subordination is the development of intergroup competition and warfare, usually as a response to stressful ecological and social circumstances." Bonnie S. Anderson and Judith P. Zinsser, *A History of Their Own: Women in Europe from Prehistory to the Present* (New York: Perennial Library, 1988), Vol. 1, p. 5.

10. This has been a traditional argument for the primacy of outward-turned, aggressive modes for behavior, one glorified by Nietzsche as the birthright of man. More recently it has taken on a more negative, ecological cast in such feminist writers as Peggy Reeves Sanday, *Female Power and Male Dominance: On the Origins of Sexual Inequality* (Cambridge, England: Cambridge University Press, 1981).

11. Lerner, pp. 43–45; Mumford, p. 11ff.

12. Cf. Page DuBois, *Sowing the Body: Psychoanalysis and Ancient Representations of Women* (Chicago: University of Chicago Press, 1988).

13. Cf. Lerner, p. 198. "The development of monotheism in the Book of Genesis was an enormous advance of human beings in the direction of abstract thought and the definition of universally valid symbols. It is a tragic accident of history that this advance occurred in a social setting and under circumstances which strengthened and affirmed patriarchy. Thus, the very process of symbol-making occurred in a form which marginalized women."

14. Cf. Pauline Fowler, "The Public and the Private in Architecture: A Feminist Critique," *Women's Studies International Forum,* Vol. 7, no. 6 (1984), pp. 449–54.

15. Cf. Vincent Scully, *Pueblo Architecture of the Southwest* (Austin: University of Texas Press, 1971); Peter Nabokov and Robert Easton, *Native American Architecture* (New York: Oxford University Press, 1989), p. 348ff. Lewis Mumford offers two possibilities for the development of cities—cooperation and gradual growth or violence and domination—and points out that Western society chose the latter. Mumford, p. 89.

16. This theory has been most significantly popularized by Georges Bataille, *The Accursed Share,* tr. Robert Hurley (New York: Zone Books, 1988 [1967]).

17. For example, "At the heart of the urban labyrinth lurked not the Minotaur, a bull-like male monster, but the female Sphinx, the `strangling,' who was so called because she strangled all those who could not answer her riddle: female sexuality, womanhood out of control, lost nature, loss of identity." Elizabeth Wilson, *The Sphinx in the City: Urban Life, the Control of Disorder, and Women* (Berkeley: University of California Press, 1991).

18. Camille Paglia, *Sexual Personae: Art and Decadence from Nefertiti to Emily Dickinson* (New York: Vintage Books, 1991 [1990]), p. 59.

19. Vincent Scully, Lectures, "History of Architecture," Yale University, 1983.

20. Mumford, p. 94.

21. Proverbs 31:22–23. For a description of the forms and importance of weaving in preindustrial societies, see Elizabeth Wayland Barber, *Women's Work: The First 20,000 Years. Women, Cloth, and Society—in Early Times* (New York: W. W. Norton & Company, 1994).

22. Hollis S. Baker, *Furniture in the Ancient World: Origins and Evolution, 3100–475 B.C.* (London: The Connoisseur, 1966).

23. Geiger, p. 41: "Auf Kreta scheint es eine lebendige und gewachsene Verwobenheit von Goettlichem und Alltag, von Wirtschaft und Kultus, von Bauen und Wohnen gegeben zu haben, und überbevölkerung ist in dieser theakratischen und gynaikokratischen Ordnung nicht zum Problem geworden. Auf unseren Suche nach von Frauen entworfenen Bauten, von Frauen genutztem Raum treffen wir hier in Kreta erstmals auf Zeugnissed eines Bauens, das nicht dem Prinzip der Machtenfaltung und Kontrolle unterliegt, sondern dem grundlegenden menschlichen Beduerfnis nach Wohnen—dazu noch in aeusserst verfeinerter Form."

24. Vincent Scully, *The Earth, the Temple, and the Gods: Greek Sacred Architecture*, rev. ed. (New York: Frederick A. Praeger, 1969 [1962]), p. 11.

25. Ibid., p. 154.

26. Eva C. Keuls, *The Reign of the Phallus: Sexual Politics in Ancient Athens* (New York, Harper & Row, Publishers, 1985), p. 38.

27. Ibid., p. 185.

28. Ibid., p. 95.

29. Ibid., p. 97.

30. Cf. Lerner, p. 206; Ann Bergren, "Educating Architecture as a `Total Woman': Programmata for an Architecture of Mêtis," *Harvard Architecture Review*, no. 8 (1991), pp. 136–59.

31. Ibid., p. 124.

32. Marilyn B. Arthur, "The Dream of a World Without Women: Poetics and the Circles of Order in the *Theogony* Prooemium," *Arethusa*, Vol. 16, no. 1–2 (1983), pp. 97–116, 111–12.

33. Ann Bergren, "The (Re)Marriage of Penelope and Odysseus Architecture Gender Philosophy," *Assemblage*, no. 21 (August 1993), pp. 7–23, 8.

34. This idea is picked up by Manuel De Landa in "Nonorganic Life," *Zone 6: Incorporations* (New York: Zone Books, 1992), pp. 129–67.

35. Cf. Mark Wigley, "Postmortem Architecture: A Taste of Derrida," *Perspecta*, Vol. 23, pp. 156–172, and also "Prosthetic Theory: The Disciplining of Architecture," *Assemblage*, Vol. 15, pp. 7–29.

36. Bergren, "(Re)Marriage," p. 19.

37. Ann Bergren, "Architecture Gender Philosophy," *Strategies of Architectural Thinking*, ed. John Whiteman, Jeffrey Kipnis, and Richard Burdett (Chicago, Chicago Institute for Architecture and Urbanism, 1992), pp. 8–46, 15.

38. Ibid., p. 23.

Chapter 3: Crossroads and Crypts

1. It should be noted, however, that there is an alternative history to crossroads. It is there, after all, that you might meet the devil and sell your soul—a legend that has entered American mythology from Yoruba. In Western tradition the crossroads is the place of decisions, confrontations, and possibilities, where beings from other worlds might appear. Might it be that the site of suppression still retains memories of that which it buried?

2. According to the feminist philosopher Judith Butler, all power is both sited and cited: "The process of that sedimentation or what we might call *materialization* will be a kind of citationality, the acquisition of being through the citing of power, a citing that establishes an originary complicity with power in the formation of the '1.'" Judith Butler, *Bodies That Matter: On the Discursive Limits of "Sex"* (New York: Routledge, 1993), p. 15.

3. Vitruvius, *The Ten Books on Architecture*, tr. Morris Hickey Morgan (New York: Dover Publications, 1960).

4. Ibid., pp. 12–14.

5. Ibid., pp. 72ff.

6. Ibid., p. 17.

7. Ibid., p. 21.

8. Ibid., p. 41.

9. Ibid., p. 186.

10. Ibid., p. 210.

11. This continues to this day, as Richard Sennett, for instance, has pointed out in his *Conscience of the Eye: The Design of Social Life of Cities* (New York: Alfred A. Knopf, 1990), pp. 230–32. Baths have also become a place that has allowed such repressed communities as gays to find and build a community.

12. Cf. Theodor Kraus, *Pompeii and Herculaneum: The Living Cities of the Dead*, tr. Robert Erich Wolf (New York: Harry N. Abrams, Inc., 1975); Robert Étienne, *La Vie Quotidienne à Pompeii* (Paris: Hachette, 1977).

13. Cf. Paul Veyne, "The Roman Empire," *A History of Private Life*, Vol. 1, *From Pagan Rome to Byzantium*, ed. Paul Veyne, tr. Arthur Goldhammer (Cambridge, Mass.: Belknap Press of Harvard University Press, 1987 [1985]), pp. 5–234.

14. The palace was described with either awe or disgust by many contemporary observers, including Suetonius and Seneca. Cf. William L. MacDonald, *The Architecture of the Roman Empire* (New Haven, Conn.: Yale University Press, 1982), p. 41ff.

15. Cf. Pierre Grimal, *Les Jardins Romains* (Paris: Presses Universitaires de France, 1969).

16. Cf. Chapter 6.

17. Cf. MacDonald.

18. Heinrich Wölfflin, *Principles of Art History: The Problem of the Development of Style in Later Art*, tr. M. Hottinger (New York: Dover Publications, 1929 [1917]), p. 231ff.

19. Gilles Deleuze and Félix Guattari, *A Thousand Plateaus: Capitalism and Schizophrenia*, tr. Brian Massumi (Minneapolis: University of Minnesota Press, 1987), p. 500.

20. Cf. Elise Boulding, *The Underside of History: A View of Women Through Time* (Boulder, Colo.: Westview Press, 1976), p. 316; cults, p. 357.

21. Cf. Deleuze and Guattari, pp. 474–500.

22. It was not only the Christians that used such spaces, of course. There were Jewish catacombs, and these were always spaces where those who wanted or needed to exist outside laws and buildings could find refuge. See J. Stevenson, *The Catacombs: Rediscovered Monuments of Early Christianity* (London: Thames and Hudson, 1978).

23. The cult was made official by Pope Urban II at the Council of Clermont in 1095, at the time of the First Crusade. The next century saw the rise of cathedrals dedicated to Mary, as well as the proliferation of thousands of shrines. Cf. Gerda Lerner, *The Creation of Feminist Consciousness from the Middle Ages to Eighteen-Seventy* (New York: Oxford University Press, 1993), p. 125ff. See also

Caroline Walker Bynum, *Fragmentation and Redemption: Essays of Gender and the Human Body in Medieval Religion* (New York: Zone Books, 1991).

24. Lerner, p. 75ff; the Cathars were known for their egalitarian sexual behavior, and the Albigensians were famous for their almost Zarathustrian ideas about the interdependence of male and female-forces in the world.

25. Bonnie S. Anderson and Judith P. Zinsser, *A History of Their Own: Women in Europe from Prehistory to the Present* (New York: Perennial Library, 1988), Vol. 1, p. 93.

26. Elise Boulding speculates that Jewish traders may have helped perpetuate the traditions of purdah in Mediterranean areas. Boulding, p. 345.

27. Georges Duby, ed., *A History of Private Life*, Vol. 2, *Revelations of the Medieval World*, tr. Arthur Goldhammer (Cambridge, Mass.: Belknap Press of Harvard University Press, 1988 [1985]), pp. 8–11.

28. All through the Middle Ages and into the Renaissance, women were active members of several guilds, especially those of weavers. It was in some cases not until the late sixteenth century that guild laws outlawed them from full membership, though the exclusionary movement started as early as the fourteenth century. Anderson and Zinsser, pp. 406–08.

Chapter 4: The Romance of Other Spaces

1. Michel Foucault, "Other Spaces: The Principles of Heterotopia," *Lotus*, Vol. 48–49 (1986), pp. 10–24, 12.

2. Ibid., p. 11.

3. John Hine Mundy, *Men and Women at Toulouse in the Age of the Cathars* (Toronto: Pontifical Institute of Medieval Studies, 1990); Jonathan Sumption, *The Albigensian Crusade* (London: Faber, 1978).

4. The most comprehensive description of this process remains Marc Bloch's *Feudal Society*, tr. L. A. Manyon (Chicago: University of Chicago Press, 1974 [1961]).

5. Cf. Lynn White, Jr., *Medieval Technology and Social Change* (New York: Oxford University Press, 1973).

6. Cf. Linda Eckstein, *Woman Under Monasticism* (New York: Russell & Russell, 1963).

7. Cf. Wolfgang Braunfels, *Monasteries of Western Europe: The Architecture of the Orders* (Princeton, N.J.: Princeton University Press, 1973).

8. Cf. M. Killian Hubyard, *Saint Bernard de Clairvaux: A Theory of Art from His Writings and Illustrated in Twelfth-Century Works of Art* (Lewiston, N.Y.: The Edwin Mellen Press, 1989), pp. 68, 76, 84.

9. Cf. J. van Remoorteve, *Abbayes et Beguinages de Belgique* (Brussels: Meddens, n.d.).

10. Caroline Walker Bynum, *Fragmentation and Redemption: Essays on Gender and the Human Body in Medi-eval Religion* (New York: Zone Books, 1991), p. 175.

11. Ibid., p. 123.

12. Quoted in Gerda Lerner, *The Creation of Feminist Consciousness from the Middle Ages to Eighteen-Seventy* (New York: Oxford University Press, 1993), p. 53.

13. Cf. Joan M. Ferrante, *Woman as Image in Medieval Literature from the Twelfth Century to Dante* (New York: Columbia University Press, 1975).

14. For the general nature of chivalrous society, see Georges Duby, *The Chivalrous Society*, tr. Cynthia Postan (Berkeley: University of California Press, 1977); see also Meg Bogin, *The Woman Troubadours* (New York: W. W. Norton & Co., 1976).

15. Cf. Georges Duby, "Portraits," in *A History of Private Life*, Vol. 2. *Revelations of the Medieval World,* ed. Georges Duby, tr. Arthur Goldhammer (Cambridge: Belknap Press of Harvard University Press, 1988 [1985]), pp. 33–310.

16. And thus "All was portable because one of the noble wife's duties was to supervise the moving of the household from dwelling to dwelling for reasons of economy, safety, and administration." Bonnie S. Anderson and Judith P. Zinsser, *A History of Their Own: Women in Europe from Prehistory to the Present* (New York: Perennial Library, 1988), Vol. 1, p. 287.

17. There was a feminine counter to such preconceptions that were so inbred as to be rarely questioned. The most notable of these was Christine de Pizan's 1450 *The Book of the City of Ladies*, tr. Earl Jeffrey Richards (New York: Persea Books, 1982), which proposed a highly rational and utopian society built by women.

18. "Come, Sweetheart, Come," Manuscript of Salzburg, Canterbury, and Limoges, in *The Norton Anthology of World Masterpieces* (New York: W. W. Norton, 1992), Vol. 1, p. 1266.

19. Cf. Danielle Regnier-Bohler, "Imagining the Self," *A History of Private Life*, pp. 311–94.

20. Thus current theories that link fashion and economic exploitation are, to say the least, historically shortsighted. The most egregious of these theories is the one expounded by Naomi Wolf in *The Beauty Myth: How Images of Beauty Are Used Against Women* (New York: Anchor Books, 1992 [1991]).

21. Duby, "Portraits," p. 37.

22. Cf. Michael and Ariane Batterberry, *Mirror, Mirror: A Social History of Fashion* (New York: Holt, Rinehart & Winston, 1977); Anderson J. Black, *A History of Fashion* (New York: William Morrow, 1980).

23. Teresa McLean, *Medieval Gardens* (London: Collins Publishers, 1981).

24. For the best description of the origins of the mosque tradition, see Sir Roy Strong, *Art and Power: Renaissance Festivals*, 1450–1650 (Berkeley: University of California Press, 1991).

25. Paul Veyne and Orest Ranum, "The Refuges of Intimacy," *A History of Private Life*, Vol. 3, *Passions of the Renaissance*, ed. Roger Chartier, tr. Arthur Goldhammer (Cambridge, Mass.: Belknap Press of Harvard University Press, 1989 [1986]), pp. 206–63, 227.

26. "This development did not reach its peak until the eighteenth century, by which time the family began to hold society at a distance, to push it back beyond the steadily extending zone of private life. . . . It has been said that comfort dates from this period; it was born at the same time as domesticity, privacy, and isolation, and it was one of the manifestations of these phenomena. There were no longer beds all over the house. The beds were confined to the bedrooms, which were furnished on either side of the alcove with cupboards and nooks fitted out with new toilette and hygienic equipment. In France and Italy the word *chambre* began to be used in opposition to the word *salle*— they had hitherto been more or less synonymous; the *chambre* denoted the room in which one slept, the *salle* the room in which one received visitors and ate. . . . In England the word 'room' was kept for all these functions, but a prefix was added to give precision: the dining room, the bedroom, etc." Philippe Aries, *Centuries of Childhood: A Social History of Family Life*, tr. Robert Baldick (New York: Vintage Books, 1962 [1960]), p. 398.

27. Cf. Gabriele Geiger, *Frauen, Körper, Bauten: Weibliche Wahrnehmung des Raums am Beispiel Stadt* (München: Profil Verlag, 1986), p. 127.

Chapter 5: Erecting Perfection

1. For the best description of the Western world from one of "sameness" and identity to one of difference, identity, and rationalism, see Michel Foucault, *The Order of Things: An Archaeology of the Human Sciences* (New York: Random House, 1970).

2. For a concise collection of such writings, see Ernst Cassirer, Paul Oskar Kristeller, and John Herman Randall, Jr., eds., *The Renaissance Philosophy of Man* (Chicago: University of Chicago Press, 1948).

3. Leon Battista Alberti, *On the Art of Building in Ten Books*, tr. Joseph Rykwert, Neil Leach, and Robert Tavernor (Cambridge, Mass.: MIT Press, 1991 [1486]).

4. Svetlana Alpers, *The Art of Describing: Dutch Art in the Seventeenth Century* (Chicago: University of Chicago Press, 1983), p. 41ff.

5. Leon Battista Alberti, *On Painting*, tr. John R. Spencer (New Haven, Conn.: Yale University Press, 1966), p. 56ff.

6. Leonardo da Vinci, *Treatise on Painting*, quoted in Alpers, p. 46.

7. Erwin Panofsky, in his seminal *Perspective as Symbolic Form* (New York: Zone Books, 1991 [1927]), argued that Renaissance perspective represented the particular "will to form" of Western civilization as it sought to create a space commensurate to its intellectual pretensions.

8. Alberti, *On Painting*, p. 76ff.

9. Svetlana Alpers, "Seeing as Knowing: A Dutch Connection," *Humanities in Society*, Vol. 1, pp. 147–73.

10. Alberti, *On the Art of Building*, p. 4.

11. Ibid., p. 156.

12. Ibid.

13. For Alberti's attitude toward women and how the feminine was treated as a category in Renaissance architecture, see Mark Wigley, "Untitled: The Housing of Gender," in *Sexuality & Space*, ed. Beatriz Colomina (New York: Princeton Architectural Press, 1992), pp. 326–89.

14. Rudolf Wittkower, *Architectural Principles in the Age of Humanism* (New York: W. W. Norton & Company, 1971 [1961]), p. 13ff.

15. Ibid., p. 15.

16. See also George Hersey, *Pythagorean Palaces: Magic and Architecture in the Italian Renaissance* (Ithaca, N.Y.: Cornell University Press, 1976).

17. Andrea Palladio, *The Four Books of Architecture* (New York: Dover Books, 1965 [1570]).

18. Cf. Richard A. Goldthwaite, *Private Wealth in Renaissance Florence: A Study of Four Families* (Princeton, N.J.: Princeton University Press, 1968) and *The Building of Renaissance Florence: An Economic and Social History* (Baltimore, Md.: Johns Hopkins University Press, 1980).

19. Sebastiano Serlio, *I Sette Libri del'Architettura* (Venice: 1537–57).

20. For the best summary description and interpretation of Vaux-le-Vicomte, see Vincent Scully, *Architecture: The Natural and the Manmade* (New York: St. Martin's Press, 1991), pp. 237–65.

21. Cf. Peter Thornton, *Seventeenth-Century Decoration in England, France and Holland* (New Haven, Conn.: Paul Mellon Center for British Art, 1978).

22. Cf. Joseph Rykwert, *The First Moderns: The Architects of the Eighteenth Century* (Cambridge, Mass.: MIT Press, 1980).

23. Manfredo Tafuri, *Architecture and Utopia: Design and Capitalist Development*, tr. Barbara Luigia La Penta (Cambridge, Mass.: The MIT Press, 1979 [1973]), pp. 4ff.

24. The emergence of this system is traced most coherently by David Van Zanten, "Architectural Composition at the École des Beaux-Arts from Charles Percier to Charles Garnier," *The Architecture of the École des Beaux-Arts*, ed. Arthur Drexler (New York: Museum of Modern Art, 1977), pp. 111–322. More recently Sylvia Lavin has traced the codification of architectural language as part of a wider project of creating an order system of classification in her *Quatremère de Quincy and the Invention of a Modern Language of Architecture* (Cambridge, Mass.: MIT Press, 1993).

25. Cf. Anthony Vidler, *The Writings of the Wall: Architectural Theory in the Late Enlightenment* (New York: Princeton Architectural Press, 1987), pp. 35–49.

26. Etienne-Louis Boullée, *Essai sur l'Art*, in Alberto Pérez-Gómez, *Architecture and the Crisis of Modern Science* (Cambridge, Mass.: MIT Press, 1983), p. 144.

27. Vidler; Claude-Nicolas Ledoux, *L'Architecture de C. N. Ledoux* (New York: Princeton Architectural Press, 1983 [1847]), pl. 240.

Chapter 6: The Gilded Cage

1. For this description I am indebted to Madlyn Millner Kahr, *Dutch Painting in the Seventeenth Century* (New York: Harper & Row, Publishers, 1978), pp. 185–86.

2. Simon Schama's eloquent *An Embarrassment of Riches: An Interpretation of Dutch Culture in the Golden Age* (New York: Random House, 1987) does much to set the scene here, though there are few if any English-language histories that discuss the historical forces that led to the situation of the Golden Age.

3. Van der Heyden not only was a painter of highly specific street scenes but also organized the first effective fire brigade and invented an effective fire pump.

4. Svetlana Alpers, *The Art of Describing: Dutch Art in the Seventeenth Century* (Chicago: University of Chicago Press, 1983); I am indebted to Celeste Brusati for a further explication of this text.

5. This was the perspective system illustrated by Jan Vredeman de Vries in his 1605 "Perspective," in which the single vanishing point is doubled. Ibid., pp. 57–58.

6. To this day, one of the most highly valued qualities of life in Holland is *gezelligheid*, a term that denotes the good cheer and warm feeling derived from gathering with friends or family in a cozy, well-outfitted domestic environment.

7. Cf. Peter Thornton, *Authentic Decor: The Domestic Environment, 1620–1920* (London: Weidenfeld and Nicolson, 1984), pp. 48–49.

8. Anthony Blunt, *Baroque and Rococo Architecture and Decoration* (London: Faber, 1978).

9. H. Pose, *Jahrbuch der Preuszischen Kunstsammlungen*, Vol. XL (1919), p. 161, in Fiske Kimball, *The Creation of the Rococo Decorative Style* (New York: Dover Publications, 1980 [1943]), p. 13.

10. Kimball, p. 138.

11. Choderlos de Laclos, *Les Liaisons Dangereuses*, tr. Richard Aldington (Norwalk, Conn.: New Directions Books, 1957 [1782]). The perfect perversion of this world can be found in the writings of the Marquis de Sade.

12. Cf. Mario Praz, *An Illustrated History of Interior Decoration from Pompeii to Art Nouveau* (London: Thames and Hudson, 1981), pp. 13–67.

13. Especially vehement on these issues were Joseph Addison in the *Spectator* and Voltaire. Cf. Bonnie S. Anderson and Judith P. Zinsser, *A History of Their Own: Women in Europe from Prehistory to the Present* (New York: Perennial Library, 1988), Vol. 2, p. 114.

14. Anderson and Zinsser, pp. 103–28. See also Jacques Revel, "The Uses of Civility," in *A History of Private LIfe*, Vol. 3, *Passions of the Renaissance*, ed. Roger Chartier, tr. Arthur Goldhammer (Cambridge, Mass.: Belknap Press of Harvard University Press, 1989 [1986]), pp. 167–205; Orest Ranum, "The Refugees of Intimacy," ibid., pp. 207–63.

15. Alexander Pope, *The Rape of the Lock*, Canto I, 121–36 (1717).

16. For the exclusion of women, see Anderson and Zinsser, p. 412; for the definition of the profession, see Alberto Pérez-Gómez, *Architecture and the Crisis of Modern Science* (Cambridge, Mass.: MIT Press, 1983).

17. The *Encyclopédie* was, after all, dedicated to explaining the world in a rational manner. In so doing, it destroyed intimate and sacred spaces, as well as the well-guarded secrets of the guilds, and paved the way for factory spaces.

18. One can also compare Soane's space to Thomas Jefferson's famous bedroom, a place where gadgetry took over from architecture, though here in the service of Enlightenment and male control.

Chapter 7: The Discreet Places of the Bourgeoisie

1. Theodore Dreiser, *Sister Carrie* (New York: Bantam Books, 1982 [1900]), p. 13.

2. Ibid., pp. 68–69.

3. Ibid., pp. 74–75.

4. Judith Blair, in "Private Parts in Public Places: The Case of Actresses," claims that the actress is the woman who actualizes the predicament in which the woman finds herself—namely, that she can be herself only by acting the role of the woman. Shirley Ardener, ed., *Woman and Space* (London: Croom Helm, 1981), pp. 205–28.

5. Fyodor Dostoevsky, *Crime and Punishment*, tr. Constance Garnett (New York: Bantam Books, 1981 [1866]).

6. Jean-Jacques Rousseau, *Julie, ou la Héloïse, Oeuvres Complètes*, Vol. II (Paris: Gallimard, 1959 [1761]).

7. Though Jefferson late in life moderated his opposition to cities and "manufacture," his ideal remained a rural state that governed itself through confederation. See his *Notes on the State of Virginia* (1787), in *The Portable Thomas Jefferson*, ed. Merrill D. Peterson (New York: Penguin Books, 1975), pp. 23–232, 216–17.

8. Karl Marx, Friedrich Engels, *Manifesto of the Communist Party* (1848), *Marx & Engels: Basic Writings on Politics and Philosophy,* ed. Lewis S. Feuer (Garden City, N.Y.: Doubleday Books, 1959), pp. 1–41, 10.

9. Marshall Berman, *All That Is Solid Melts into Air: The Experience of Modernity* (New York: Penguin Books, 1988), p. 13.

10. William Blake, "London," *Songs of Innocence and Experience* (London: 1794), pl. 46.

11. Frank Lloyd Wright, "The Art and Craft of the Machine," reprinted in *Frank Lloyd Wright Collected Writings,* Vol. 1 (New York: Rizzoli, 1992), pp. 68-69.

12. Mary Shelley, *Frankenstein, or, The Modern Prometheus* (New York: New American Library, 1965 [1814]); Émile Zola, *Germinal,* tr. L. W. Tancock (London: Penguin Books, 1956 [1885]).

13. Cf. Michel Foucault, *The Order of Things: An Archaeology of the Human Sciences* (New York: Random House, 1970). The notion of human beings as "standing reserve" comes from Martin Heidegger, "The Question Concerning Technology," *The Question Concerning Technology and Other Essays,* tr. William Lovitt (New York: Harper & Row Publishers, 1977), pp. 3–35.

14. Elizabeth Wilson, *The Sphinx in the City: Urban Life, the Control of Disorder, and Women* (Berkeley: University of California Press, 1991), p. 59.

15. Though there are now numerous descriptions of nineteenth-century interiors, the most thoughtful essay on their meaning remains the Introduction to Mario Praz's *An Illustrated History of Interior Decoration from Pompeii to Art Nouveau* (London: Thames and Hudson, 1981).

16. Of special note are A. W. N. Pugin's *Contrasts; or, a Parallel Between the Noble Edifices of the Fourteenth and Fifteenth Centuries, and Similar Buildings of the Present Day* (London: Dolman, 1841), John Ruskin's *The Two Paths in Art* (London: 1859), and Charles Eastlake's *Hints on Household Taste in Furniture, Upholstery and Other Details* (London: Longmans, Green and Co., 1872).

17. Cf. Anthony Vidler, *The Writings of the Walls: Architectural Theory in the Late Enlightenment* (New York: Princeton Architectural Press, 1987), pp. 24–28.

18. Harvey Green, lecture at the University of Cincinnati, March 13, 1984. Green expands on this notion in *The Light of the Home: An Intimate View of the Lives of Women in Victorian America* (New York: Pantheon Books, 1983).

19. Henry James, *The Spoils of Poynton* (New York: Penguin Books, 1981 [1897]), pp. 18–19.

20. Ibid., p. 40.

21. Charlotte Perkins Gilman, *The Man-made World or Our Androcentric Culture* (New York: Charlton Company, 1911); she also wrote the utopian novel *Herland* (New York: Pantheon Books, 1978 [1915]).

22. Charlotte Perkins Gilman, *The Yellow Wallpaper* (New York: Bantam Books, 1989).

23. Cf. Gwendolyn Wright, *Building the Dream: A Social History of Housing in America* (Cambridge, Mass.: MIT Press, 1983), pp. 96ff; Alan Gowans, *The Comfortable House: North American Suburban Architecture, 1890–1930* (Cambridge, Mass.: MIT Press, 1986).

24. Raymond Williams has argued that nineteenth-century distinctions between male and female, or nature and city, were deliberate tactics meant to allow for dynamic transformation without challenging the social order. For a discussion of this position within a feminist context, see Ludmilla Jordanova, *Sexual Visions: Images of Gender in Science and Medicine Between the Eighteenth and the Twentieth Centuries* (Madison: University of Wisconsin Press, 1989), esp. p. 22.

25. Griselda Pollock, the most perceptive feminist historian of nineteenth-century art, argues that women were allowed to enter the privileged space of painting only as actresses or spectators and thus that there is a "coincidence between the spaces of modernity

and the spaces of masculinity as they intersect in the territory of cross-class sexual exchange." Griselda Pollock, "Modernity and the Spaces of Femininity," *The Expanding Discourse: Feminism and Art History*, ed. Norma Broude and Mary D. Garrard (New York: Icon Editions, 1992), pp. 245–67, 261.

26. Cf. Walter Benjamin, "Paris, Capital of Nineteenth Century," *Reflections: Essays, Aphorisms, Autobiographical Writings*, tr. Edmund Jephcott (New York: Schocken Books, 1978), pp. 146–62.

27. Wilson, p. 16.

28. Cf. Gunther Barth, *City People: The Rise of Modern City Culture* (New York: Oxford University Press, 1980), p. 6ff.

29. William H. Wilson, *The City Beautiful Movement* (Baltimore: Johns Hopkins University Press, 1989).

30. What became known as the Moynihan Report was originally the U.S. Department of Labor's Office of Policy Planning and Research, *The Negro Family: A Case for National Action* (Washington, D.C.: United States Government Printing Office, 1965).

31. Wilson, p. 41.

Chapter 8: At Home in the Maelstrom of Modernity

1. Catharine Beecher and Harriet Beecher Stowe, *The American Woman's Home: Or, Principles of Domestic Science* (New York: J. B. Ford & Company, 1869).

2. Ibid., unnumbered plate.

3. Ibid., p. 76.

4. Ibid., p. 25.

5. This argument has been made by Marion Roberts in *Living in a Man-made World: Gender Assumptions in Modern Housing Design* (London: Routledge, 1991), though she also points out that cleaning and tidying were ways of ordering the world rather than merely creating hygiene.

6. Neil Levine, "The Romantic Ideal of Architectural Legibility: Henri Labrouste and the Neo-Grec," in *The Architecture of the École des Beaux-Arts*, ed. Arthur Drexler (New York: Museum of Modern Art, 1977), pp. 325–415.

7. Ruth Schwartz Cowan, *More Work for Mother: The Ironies of Household Technology from the Open Hearth to the Microwave* (New York: Basic Books, 1983), p. 101.

8. John Ruskin, "The Two Paths in Art; Being Lectures on Art, and Its Application to Decoration and Manufacture, Delivered in 1858–9," *The Works of John Ruskin* (New York: John Wiley & Sons, 1879), Vol. 12.

9. The influence of Ruskin is traced in great detail by Roger Stein in *John Ruskin and Aesthetic Thought in America, 1840–1900* (Cambridge, Mass.: Harvard University Press, 1967).

10. Ruskin, p. 108.

11. Cf. Peter A. Kropotkin, *Selected Writings on Anarchism and Revolution*, ed. Martin A. Miller (Cambridge, Mass.: MIT Press, 1970).

12. This vision remains alive today in some startling ways, ranging from the surviving hippie communes of Vermont and New Mexico to the futuristic visions of New York architect Lebbeus Woods, who has for the last five years been drawing anarchist communities floating through the sky above Paris or burrowing below the sidewalks of Berlin.

13. The best history of such movements is Dolores Hayden's *Seven American Utopias: The Architecture of Communitarian Socialism, 1790–1975* (Cambridge, Mass.: MIT Press, 1976) and also her *The Grand Domestic Revolution: A History of Feminist Designs for American Homes, Neighborhoods, and Cities* (Cambridge, Mass.: MIT Press, 1981).

14. Cf. Gillian Naylor, *The Arts and Crafts Movement: A Study of Its Sources, Ideals, and Influences on Design Theory* (London: Trefoil Publishers, 1990); William Morris, *The Decorative Arts: Their Relations to Modern Life & Progresses*, ed. F.-A. Schmidt-Kungemüller (Osnabrück: O. Zeller, 1975).

NOTES

15. Walter Gropius, "Principles of Bauhaus Production," in *Programs and Manifestoes on 20th-Century Architecture,* ed. Ulrich Conreds, tr. Michael Bullock (Cambridge, Mass.: MIT Press, 1970), pp. 95–96.

16. The result of Behrens's work was an *Industriekultur* that still remains the paradigm of how a corporation can create a complete environment for its workers and its customers. The "masculinity" of this culture was, according to Behrens, one of its strongest features. See Tillmans Buddensieg, *Industriekultur: Peter Behrens and the AEG,* tr. Iain Boyd White (Cambridge, Mass.: MIT Press, 1984).

17. Walter Gropius, "Programme of the Staatliches Bauhaus in Weimar," in *Programs and Manifestoes,* pp. 49–53, 49.

18. Theo van Doesburg, "Towards a Plastic Architecture," in *Programs and Manifestoes,* pp. 78–80, esp. p. 78; it should be noted, however, how important the grid (the "rectangles" without individuality) still are in this canonical statement of modernism.

19. For a good description of how artists such as van Doesburg envisioned space, see Nancy J. Troy, *The De Stijl Environment* (Cambridge, Mass.: MIT Press, 1983).

20. Cf. Selim O. Khan-Magomedov, *Pioneers of Soviet Architecture,* tr. Alexander Lieven (New York: Rizzoli International Publications, 1987).

21. Cf. Beatriz Colomina, "The Split Wall: Domestic Voyeurism," *Sexuality & Space,* ed. Beatriz Colomina (New York: Princeton Architectural Press, 1992), pp. 72–128.

22. Excerpts from "The Work of Art in the Age of Mechanical Reproduction" in *Illuminations* by Walter Benjamin, copyright ©1955 by Suhrkamp Verlag, Frankfurt a.m.; English translation copyright ©1968 by Harcourt Brace & Company, pp.217-51, esp. 263-37.

23. Ibid., p. 240.

24. Ibid., p. 242.

25. Adolf Loos, "Ornament and Crime," in *Programs and Manifestoes,* pp. 19–24.

26. This has been argued most persuasively by Kenneth Frampton in his essay "Seven Points Towards a Critical Regionalism," *The Anti-Aesthetic: Essays on Postmodern Culture,* ed. Hal Foster (Seattle: Bay Press, 1983), pp. 16–30.

27. Frank Lloyd Wright, *The Natural House* (New York: Horizon Press, 1954).

28. Manfredo Tafuri, *Architecture and Utopia: Design and Capitalist Development,* tr. Barbara Luigia La Penta (Cambridge, Mass.: 1979 [1973]).

29. Edith Wharton and Ogden Codman, Jr., *The Decoration of Houses* (New York: W. W. Norton & Co., 1978 [1897]), n.p.

30. Emily Post made the link between house design and etiquette explicit. Cf. Leslie Kanes Weisman, *Discrimination by Design: A Feminist Critique of the Man-made Environment* (Urbana: University of Chicago Press, 1992), p. 95.

31. Jeffrey L. Meikle, *Twentieth Century Limited: Industrial Design in America, 1925–1939* (Philadelphia: Temple University Press, 1979), p. 170.

32. Ibid., p. 185.

33. That is certainly the way Charles Jencks, who coined the term, defines "postmodernism" in his seminal *The Language of Postmodern Architecture* (New York: Rizzoli International Publications, 1977).

34. *Dynasty,* produced by Aaron Spelling and Doug Kramer, 1983–84.

Chapter 9: Constructing Sex

1. For the most trenchant critique of the way sexual discrimination and even danger is built into our physical environment, see Leslie Kanes Weisman, *Discrimination by Design: A Feminist Critique of the Man-made Environment* (Urbana: University of Chicago Press, 1992): "In associating the workplace with male power, impersonalization, and rationality, and the home with female passivity, nurturance, and emotionalism, distinctly different behaviors in public and private settings, and in women and men, have been fostered. The result is the creation of a symbolic universe that holds women privately responsible for the care, repair, and renewal of human life in a world they do not essentially control, and assigns to men the public responsibility for running the houses of government where they have become

more concerned with the nuclear race than the human race. Under these conditions, we can no longer afford to confine the 'female attributes' to the home and family; for men, insofar as they embody this patriarchal dichotomy, have created a world that is dangerous for everyone, including themselves. Healing this schism through new spatial arrangements that encourage the integration of work and play, intellect and feeling, action and compassion, is a survival imperative" (p. 20).

2. Cf. Renee Hirschorn, "Essential Objects and the Sacred: Interior and Exterior Space in an Urban Greek Locality," *Woman and Space: Ground Rules and Social Maps*, ed. Shirley Ardener (London: Croom Helm, 1981), pp. 72–88.

3. The result of such policies is what the critic Mike Davis has called an "ecology of fear" that creates a vicious cycle of crime, repression, and paranoia. See his *City of Quartz: Excavating the Future in Los Angeles* (London: Verso Press, 1990) and "Beyond Blade Runner: Urban Control. The Ecology of Fear," *Open Pamphlet*, No. 23 (December, 1992).

4. Dolores Hayden, "What Would a Non-Sexist City Be Like? Speculations on Housing, Urban Design, and Human Work," *Women and the American City*, ed. Catherine R. Stimpson (Chicago, University of Chicago Press, 1981), pp. 167–184, and *Redesigning the American Dream: The Future of Housing, Work, and Family Life* (New York: W. W. Norton & Company, 1984). Hayden quotes some of the many admirable alternatives to such a scheme that have been proposed both here and in Europe within the last ten years. It should be noted that none of them has, to my knowledge, been successfully constructed here.

5. For a fairly complete survey of such suggestions, see Barbara Oldershaw, "Constructive Criticism of the Man-made Environment: Feminist Approaches to Buildings and Cities, 1970–1986," master's thesis, UCLA, 1987.

6. Several comprehensive statements of this theory are currently in process. See also Andres Duany and Elizabeth Plater-Zyberk, eds., *Towns and Town-Making Principles* (Cambridge, Mass.: Harvard University Graduate School of Architecture, 1991), and Peter Calthorpe, *The Next American Metropolis: Ecology, Community and the American Dream* (New York: Princeton Architectural Press, 1993).

7. There is no comprehensive catalog or monograph on the work of Gordon Matta-Clark. Most of the work is collected in Mary Jane Jacob, *Gordon Matta-Clark: A Retrospective* (Chicago: Museum of Contemporary Art, Chicago, 1985).

8. Cf. Elizabeth Diller and Ricardo Scofidio, *Flesh* (New York: Princeton Architectural Press, 1984).

9. Victor Burgin, "Geometry and Abjection," *AA Files*, No. 15 (Summer, 1988), pp. 35–41; Laura Mulvey, "Visual Pleasure and Narrative Cinema," *Visual and Other Pleasures* (Bloomington: Indiana University Press, 1989), pp. 14–26; they base their work on readings in E. H. Gombrich, Jacques Lacan, and Roland Barthes.

10. Cf. Mark Wigley, *Deconstruction and Architecture* (Cambridge, Mass.: MIT Press, 1994).

11. Wolf Prix, lecture at the Southern California Institute of Architecture, July 18, 1992.

12. These drawings form a trilogy, called "Aerial Paris," "Underground Berlin," and "Heterotopia," created in the late 1980s. For a complete description, as well as a general discussion of the place of this kind of work in the architectural culture, see my *Violated Perfection: Architecture and the Fragmentation of the Modern* (New York: Rizzoli International Publications, 1990).

13. Lebbeus Woods, *Architecture and War*, unpublished drawing suite, 1993.

14. It is interesting to note that many of this country's leading theoreticians in the field are women (Dolores Hayden, Gwendolyn Wright, Sylvia Lavin, Beatriz Colomina, Catherine Ingraham, Ann Bergren), while the profession remains male-dominated.

15. "The woman who gave birth, therefore, did not know the pride of creation; she felt herself the plaything of obscure forces, and the painful ordeal of child-birth seemed a useless or even trouble-some accident. But in any case giving birth and suckling are not *activities*, they are natural functions; no project is involved; and that is why woman found in them no reason for a lofty affirmation of her existence—she submitted pas-sively to her biologic fate. The domestic labors that fell to her lot because they were reconcilable with the cares of maternity imprisoned her in repetition and immanence; they were repeated from day to day in an identical form, which was perpetuated almost without change from century to century; they produced nothing new. Man's case was radically different; he furnished support for the group, not in the manner of worker bees by a simple vital process, through biological behavior, but by means of acts that transcended animal nature. *Homo faber* has from the begin-ning of time been an inventor: the stick and the club with which he armed him-self to knock down fruits and to slaughter animals became forthwith instruments for enlarging his grasp upon the world. He did not limit himself to bringing home the fish he caught in the sea: first he had to conquer the watery realm by means of the dugout canoe fashioned from a tree-trunk; to get at the riches of the world he annexed the world itself. In this activity he put his power to the test; he set up goals and opened up roads toward them; in brief, he found self-realization as an existent. To maintain, he created; he burst out of the present, he opened the future. This is the reason why fishing and hunting expeditions had a sacred character. Their successes were cele-brated with festivals and triumphs, and therein man gave recognition to his human estate. Today he still manifests this pride when he has built a dam or a skyscraper or an atomic pile. He has worked not merely to conserve the world as given; he has broken through its tiers, he has laid down the founda-tions of a new future." Simone de Beauvoir, *The Second Sex*, ed. and tr. H. M. Parshley (New York: Vintage Books, 1989 [1949]), p. 63.

16. Cf. Irene Diamon and Gloria Feman Oren-stein, eds., *Reweaving the World: The Emergence of Ecofeminism* (San Fran-cisco: Sierra Club Books, 1990).

17. Excerpts from *Simians, Cyborgs, and Woman* (1981), by Donna Haraway; reprinted by permission of the publisher, Routledge, New York, p. 181.

18. Ibid., p. 177.

19. In this she mirrors the work of Judith Butler (see below) and especially Michel Foucault, whose magisterial *The History of Sexuality*, tr. Robert Hurley (New York: Vintage Books, 1990 [1976]), remains the classic text underlying the thinking of all of the writers mentioned in this chapter.

20. Haraway, pp. 149–51.

21. Ibid., p. 170.

22. Ibid., p. 225.

23. Ibid., pp. 173, 176.

24. Luce Irigaray, *An Ethics of Sexual Differ-ence*, tr. Carolyn Burke and Gillian C. Gill (Ithaca, N.Y.: Cornell University Press, 1993 [1984]), p. 51.

25. Ibid., p. 198.

26. Ibid., p. 214; Irigaray uses the Lacanian term *jouissance* to mean both "play" and "pleasure or delight."

27. Judith Butler, *Bodies That Matter: On the Discursive Limits of "Sex"* (New York: Routledge, 1993), p. 2ff.

28. Ibid., pp. 1–2.

29. Ibid., p. 3.

30. Ibid., p. 13ff.

31. Ibid., p. 2.

Selected Bibliography

Abu-Lughod. "Designing a City for All." *Planning, Women and Change,* edited by K. Hapgood and J. Getzels. Chicago: American Planning Association, 1974, pp. 37–42.

Agrest, Diana I. *Architecture from Without: Theoretical Framings for a Critical Practice.* Cambridge, Mass.: MIT Press, 1991.

Alberti, Leon Battista. *On the Art of Building in Ten Books.* Translated by Joseph Rykwert, Neil Leach, and Robert Tavernor. Cambridge, Mass.: MIT Press, 1991 (1486).

———. *On Painting.* Translated by John R. Spencer. New Haven, Conn.: Yale University Press, 1966.

Alpers, Svetlana. *The Art of Describing: Dutch Art in the Seventeenth Century.* Chicago: University of Chicago Press, 1983.

———. "Seeing as Knowing: A Dutch Connection." *Humanities in Society,* Vol. 1, (1979) pp. 147–73.

Anderson, Bonnie S., and Judith P. Zinsser. *A History of Their Own: Women in Europe from Prehistory to the Present.* New York: Perennial Library, 1988. 2 vols.

Ardener, Shirley, ed. *Defining Females: The Nature of Women in Society.* New York: John Wiley & Sons, 1978.

———. *Ground Rules and Social Maps for Women: An Introduction.* London: Billing and Sons, 1981.

Aries, Philippe. *Centuries of Childhood: A Social History of Family Life.* Translated by Robert Baldick. New York: Vintage Books, 1962 (1960).

Arthur, Marilyn B. "The Dream of a World Without Women: Poetics and the Circles of Order in the Theogony Prooemium." *Arethusa,* Vol. 16, nos. 1–2 (1983), pp. 97–116.

Attfield, Judy, and Pat Kirkham, eds. *A View from the Interior: Feminism, Women and Design.* London: Women's Press, 1989.

Baker, Hollis S. *Furniture in the Ancient World: Origins and Evolution, 3100–475 B.C.* London: The Connoisseur, 1966.

Barber, Elizabeth Wayland. *Women's Work: The First 20,000 Years—Women, Cloth, and Society in Early Times.* New York: W. W. Norton & Company, 1994.

Baring, Anne, and Jules Cashford. *The Myth of the Goddess: Evolution of an Image.* New York: Penguin
   Books, 1993.

Barth, Gunther. *City People: The Rise of Modern City Culture.* New York: Oxford University Press, 1980.

Batterberry, Michael and Ariane. *Mirror, Mirror: A Social History of Fashion.* New York: Holt,
   Rinehart & Winston, 1977.

Beauvoir, Simone de. *The Second Sex.* Translated and edited by H. M. Parshley. New York:
   Vintage Books, 1989 (1949).

Beecher, Catharine. *Treatise on Domestic Economy, for the Use of Young Ladies at Home and at School.*
   Boston: Thomas H. Webb, 1842.

———, and Harriet Beecher Stowe. *The American Woman's Home: Or, Principles of Domestic Science.*
   New York: J. B. Ford & Company, 1869.

Benjamin, Walter. "Paris, Capital of the Nineteenth Century." *Reflections: Essays, Aphorisms,
   Autobiographical Writings.* Translated by Edmund Jephcott. New York: Schocken Books,
   1978, pp. 146–62.

———. "The Work of Art in the Age of Mechanical Production." *Illuminations.* Translated by Harry Zohn.
   New York: Schocken Books, 1969 (1932), pp. 217–51.

Bergren, Ann. "Architecture Gender Philosophy." *Strategies of Architectural Thinking.* Edited by
   John Whiteman, Jeffrey Kipnis, and Richard Burdett. Chicago: Chicago Institute for
   Architecture and Urbanism, 1992, pp. 8–46.

———. "Educating Architecture as a 'Total Woman': *Programmata* for an Architecture of *Mêtis.*"
   Harvard Architectural Review, No. 8 [1991] pp. 136–59.

———. "The (Re)Marriage of Penelope and Odysseus Architecture Gender Philosophy." *Assemblage,*
   No. 21 (August 1993), pp. 7–23.

Berman, Marshall. *All That Is Solid Melts into Air: The Experience of Modernity.* New York: Penguin Books,
   1988.

Birch, Eugenie, ed. *The Unsheltered Woman.* New Brunswick, N.J.: Rutgers University Center for Urban Policy
   Research, 1985.

Boulding, Elise. *The Underside of History: A View of Women Through Time.* Boulder, Colo.: Westview Press, 1976.

Butler, Judith. *Bodies That Matter: On the Discursive Limits of "Sex."* New York: Routledge, 1993.

———. *Gender Trouble: Feminism and the Subversion of Identity.* New York: Routledge, 1990.

Bynum, Caroline Walker. *Fragmentation and Redemption: Essays on Gender and the Human Body in Medieval Religion.* New York: Zone Books, 1991.

Chartier, Roger, ed. *A History of Private Life,* Vol 3, *Passions of the Renaissance.* Translated by Arthur Goldhammer. Cambridge, Mass.: Belknap Press of Harvard University Press, 1989 (1986).

Chodorow, Nancy. *The Reproduction of Mothering: Psychoanalysis and the Sociology of Gender.* Berkeley: University of California Press, 1978.

Cock, Elizabeth Lindquist, and Estelle Jussim. "Machismo in American Architecture." *Feminist Art Journal,* Vol. 3 (Spring 1974), pp. 8–10.

Colomina, Beatriz. "The Split Wall: Domestic Voyeurism." *Sexuality & Space.* Edited by Beatriz Colomina. New York: Princeton Architectural Press, 1992, pp. 72–128.

Conrads, Ulrich, ed. *Programs and Manifestoes on 20th-Century Architecture.* Translated by Michael Bullock. Cambridge, Mass.: MIT Press, 1970.

Cowan, Ruth Schwartz. *More Work for Mother: The Ironies of Household Technology from the Open Hearth to the Microwave.* New York: Basic Books, 1983.

Cunningham, Clark E. "Order in the Atoni House." *Right and Left: Essays in Dual Symbolic Classification.* Edited by Rodney Needham. Chicago: University of Chicago Press, 1973.

Dear, Michael, and Jennifer Wolch. "How Territory Shapes Social Life." *The Power of Geography.* Boston: Unwin Hyman, 1989, pp. 3–18.

Deleuze, Gilles, and Félix Guattari. *A Thousand Plateaus: Capitalism and Schizophrenia.* Translated by Brian Massumi. Minneapolis: University of Minnesota Press, 1987.

Derrida, Jacques. "Plato's Pharmacy." *Disseminations.* Translated by Barbara Johnson. Chicago: University of Chicago Press, 1981 (1972), pp. 61–172.

Dreiser, Theodore. *Sister Carrie*. New York: Bantam Books, 1982 (1900).

DuBois, Page. *Sowing the Body: Psychoanalysis and Ancient Representations of Women*. Chicago: University of Chicago Press, 1988.

Duby, Georges. *The Chivalrous Society*. Translated by Cynthia Postan. Berkeley: University of California Press, 1977.

———, ed. *A History of Private Life: Revelations of the Medieval World*. Translated by Arthur Goldhammer. Cambridge, Mass.: Belknap Press of Harvard University Press, 1988 (1985). 2 vols.

Ecker, Gisela, ed. *Feminist Aesthetics*. Translated by Harriet Anderson. Boston: Beacon Press, 1986.

Eckstein, Linda. *Woman Under Monasticism*. New York: Russell & Russell, 1963.

Erikson, Erik. "Inner and Outer Space: Reflections on Womanhood." *Daedalus*, Vol. 93 (1964), p. 582ff.

Faegre, Torvald. *Tents: Architecture of the Nomads*. Garden City, N.Y.: Anchor Books, 1979.

Fausto-Sterling, Anne. *Myths of Gender: Biological Theories of Women and Men*. New York: Basic Books, 1985.

Ferrante, Joan M. *Woman as Image in Medieval Literature from the Twelfth Century to Dante*. New York: Columbia University Press, 1975.

Foucault, Michel. *The History of Sexuality*, Vol. 1, *An Introduction*. Translated by Robert Hurley. New York: Vintage Books, 1990 (1976).

———. "Other Spaces: The Principles of Heterotopia." *Lotus*, Vol. 48–49 (1986), pp. 10–24.

Fowler, Pauline. "The Public and the Private in Architecture: A Feminist Critique." *Women's Studies International Forum*, Vol. 7, No. 6 (1984), pp. 449–54.

Geiger, Gabriele. *Frauen, Körper, Bauten: Weibliche Wahrnehmung des Raums am Beispiel Stadt*. München: Profil Verlag, 1986.

Gilman, Charlotte Perkins. *The Man-made World or Our Androcentric Culture*. New York: Charlton Company, 1911.

———. *The Yellow Wallpaper.* New York: Bantam Books, 1989 (1892).

Goldthwaite, Richard A. *The Building of Renaissance Florence: An Economic and Social History.* Baltimore: Johns Hopkins University Press, 1980.

Gottner-Abendroth, Heide. *Die Tanzende Gottin: Prinzipien einer Matriarchalen Aesthetik.* München: Verlag Frauenoffensive, 1982.

Green, Harvey. *The Light of the Home: An Intimate View of the Lives of Women in Victorian America.* New York: Pantheon Books, 1983.

Haraway, Donna J. *Simians, Cyborgs, and Women: The Reinvention of Nature.* New York: Routledge, 1991.

Hayden, Dolores. *The Grand Domestic Revolution: A History of Feminist Designs for American Homes, Neighborhoods and Cities.* Cambridge, Mass.: MIT Press, 1981.

———. "Skyscraper Seduction, Skyscraper Rape." *Heresies,* Vol. 2 (May 1977), pp. 108–115.

———. "What Would a Non-Sexist City Be Like? Speculations on Housing, Urban Design, and Human Work." *Women and the American City.* Edited by Catherine R. Stimpson. Chicago: University of Chicago Press, 1981.

Hersey, George. *Pythagorean Palaces: Magic and Architecture in the Italian Renaissance.* Ithaca, N.Y.: Cornell University Press, 1976.

Higonnet, Anne. "Secluded Vision. Images of Feminine Experience in Nineteenth-Century Europe." *The Expanding Discourse: Feminism and Art History.* Edited by Norma Broude and Mary D. Garrard. New York: Icon Editions, 1992, pp. 171–85.

Ingraham, Catherine. "Initial Properties: Architecture and the Space of the Line." *Sexuality & Space.* Edited by Beatriz Colomina. New York: Princeton Architectural Press, 1992, pp. 254–71.

Irigaray, Luce. *An Ethics of Sexual Difference.* Translated by Carolyn Burke and Gillian C. Gill. Ithaca, N.Y.: Cornell University Press, 1993 (1984).

———. *Sexes and Genealogies.* Translated by Gillian C. Gill. New York: Columbia University Press, 1993.

James, Henry. *The Spoils of Poynton.* New York: Penguin Books, 1981 (1897).

Jordanova, Ludmilla. *Sexual Visions: Images of Gender in Science and Medicine Between the Eighteenth and the Twentieth Centuries*. Madison: University of Wisconsin Press, 1989.

Keuls, Eva C. *The Reign of the Phallus: Sexual Politics in Ancient Athens*. New York: Harper & Row, Publishers, 1985.

Khan-Magomedov, Selim O. *Pioneers of Soviet Architecture*. Translated by Alexander Lieven. New York: Rizzoli International Publications, 1987.

Kimball, Fiske. *The Creation of the Rococo Decorative Style.* New York: Dover Publications, 1980 (1943).

Laclos, Choderlos de. *Les Liaisons Dangereuses*. Translated by Richard Aldington. Norfolk, Conn.: New Directions Books, 1957 (1982).

Laqueur, Thomas. *Making Sex: Body and Gender from the Greeks to Freud*. Cambridge, Mass.: Harvard University Press, 1990.

Lawrence, Roderick J. "Domestic Space and Society: A Cross Cultural Study." *Comparative Studies in Society and History*, Vol. 24 (January 1982), pp. 104–30.

Lefebvre, Henri. *Critique of Everyday Life* [1947], Vol. 1. Translated by John Moore. London: Verso, 1991.

Lerner, Gerda. *The Creation of Feminist Consciousness from the Middle Ages to Eighteen-Seventy*. New York: Oxford University Press, 1993.

———. *The Creation of Patriarchy*. New York: Oxford University Press, 1986.

Lévi-Strauss, Claude. *The Elementary Structures of Kinship*. Translated by James Harle Bell and John Richard von Sturmer. Boston: Beacon Press, 1969.

Luther, Martin. *Conversations with Luther: Selections from Recently Published Sources of the Table Talk*. Translated and edited by Preserved Smith and Herbert Percival Gallinger. New Canaan, Conn.: Keats Publishing, 1979.

McCorquodale, Charles. *History of the Interior*. New York: Vendome Press, 1983.

McDowell, L. "Towards an Understanding of Gender Division of Urban Space." *Society and Space*, Vol. 1 (1983), pp. 59–72.

McGee, Celia. "Painting the Inward Scene." Unpublished manuscript, 1984.

Marc, Olivier. *The Psychology of the House*. London: Thames and Hudson, 1977.

Meikle, Jeffrey L. *Twentieth Century Limited: Industrial Design in America, 1925–1939*. Philadelphia: Temple University Press, 1979.

Mumford, Lewis. *The City in History: Its Origins, Its Transformations, and Its Prospects*. New York: Harcourt Brace Jovanovich, 1989 (1961).

Naylor, Gillian. *The Arts & Crafts Movement: A Study of Its Sources, Ideals, and Influences on Design Theory*. London: Trefoil Publishers, 1990.

Oldershaw, Barbara. "Constructive Criticism of the Man-made Environment: Feminist Approaches to Buildings and Cities, 1970–1986." Master's thesis, University of California at Los Angeles, 1987.

Ortner, Sherry B. "Is Female to Male as Nature Is to Culture?" *Feminist Studies*, Vol. 1, No. 2 (Fall 1972), pp. 5–31.

Paglia, Camille. *Sexual Personae. Art and Decadence from Nefertiti to Emily Dickinson*. New York: Vintage Books, 1991 (1990).

Palladio, Andrea. *The Four Books of Architecture*. New York: Dover Books, 1965 (1570).

Panofsky, Erwin. *Perspective as Symbolic Form*. Translated by Christopher S. Wood. New York: Zone Books, 1991 (1927).

Papanek, Hanna. "Purdah: Separate Worlds and Symbolic Shelter." *Comparative Studies in Society and History*, Vol. 15 (June 1973), pp. 289–325.

Parker, Rozsika. *The Subversive Stitch: Embroidery and the Making of the Feminine*. New York: Routledge, 1989.

Pérez-Gómez, Alberto. *Architecture and the Crisis of Modern Science*. Cambridge, Mass.: MIT Press, 1983.

Pizan, Christine de. *The Book of the City of Ladies*. Translated by Earl Jeffrey Richards. New York: Persea, 1982 (1450).

Pollock, Griselda. "Modernity and the Spaces of Femininity." *The Expanding Discourse: Feminism and Art History*. Edited by Norma Broude and Mary D. Garrard. New York: Icon Editions 1992, pp. 245–67.

Ponte, Alessandra. "Architecture and Phallocentrism in Richard Payne Knight's Theory." *Sexuality & Space*. Edited by Beatriz Colomina. New York: Princeton Architectural Press, 1992, pp. 272–305.

Praz, Mario. *An Illustrated History of Interior Decoration from Pompeii to Art Nouveau*. London: Thames and Hudson, 1981.

Preziosi, Donald. *Minoan Architectural Design: Formation and Signification*. New York: Mouton Publishers, 1983.

Remoorteve, J. van. *Abbayes et Beguinages de Belgique*. Bruxelles: Meddens, n.d.

Roberts, Marion. *Living in a Man-made World: Gender Assumptions in Modern Housing Design*. London: Routledge, 1991.

Ruskin, John. "The Two Paths in Art; Being Lectures on Art, and Its Application to Decoration and Manufacture, Delivered in 1858–9." *The Works of John Ruskin*, Vol. XII. New York: John Wiley & Sons, 1879.

Rykwert, Joseph. *The First Moderns: The Architects of the Eighteenth Century*. Cambridge, Mass.: MIT Press, 1980.

———. *On Adam's House in Paradise: The Idea of the Primitive Hut in Architectural Theory*. Cambridge, Mass.: MIT Press, 1981.

Saegert, Susan. "Masculine Cities and Feminine Suburbs: Polarized Ideas, Contradictory Realities." *Women and the American City*. Edited by Catherine Stimpson. Chicago: University of Chicago Press, 1981.

Sanday, Peggy Reeves. *Female Power and Male Dominance: On the Origins of Sexual Inequality*. Cambridge, England: Cambridge University Press, 1981.

Scully, Vincent. *Architecture: The Natural and the Manmade*. New York: St. Martin's Press, 1991.

———. *The Earth, the Temple, and the Gods: Greek Sacred Architecture*, revised edition. New York: Frederick A. Praeger, 1969 (1962).

Semper, Gottfried. *The Four Elements of Architecture and Other Writings*. Translated by Harry Francis Mallgrave and Wolfgang Herrman. Cambridge, England: Cambridge University Press, 1989.

Spain, Daphne. *Gendered Spaces*. Chapel Hill: University of North Carolina Press, 1992.

Strong, Sir Roy. *Art and Power: Renaissance Festivals, 1450–1650*. Berkeley: University of California Press, 1981.

Tafuri, Manfredo. *Architecture and Utopia: Design and Capitalist Development*. Translated by Barbara Luigia La Penta. Cambridge, Mass.: MIT Press, 1979 (1973).

Thornton, Peter. *Authentic Decor: The Domestic Interior, 1620–1920*. London: Weidenfeld and Nicolson, 1984.

———. *Seventeenth-Century Interior Decoration in England, France and Holland*. New Haven, Conn.: Paul Mellon Center for Studies in British Art, 1978.

Todd, Ian A. *Çatal Hüyük in Perspective*. Menlo Park, Calif.: Cummings Publications Co., 1976.

Troy, Nancy J. *The De Stijl Environment*. Cambridge, Mass.: MIT Press, 1983.

Veyne, Paul, ed. *A History of Private Life*, Vol. 1, *From Pagan Rome to Byzantium*. Translated by Arthur Goldhammer. Cambridge, Mass.: Belknap Press of Harvard University Press, 1987 (1985).

Vidler, Anthony. *The Architectural Uncanny: Essays in the Modern Unhomely*. Cambridge, Mass.: MIT Press, 1992.

———. *The Writing of the Walls: Architectural Theory in the Late Enlightenment*. New York: Princeton Architectural Press, 1987.

Vitruvius. *The Ten Books on Architecture*. Translated by Morris Hickey Morgan. New York: Dover Publications, 1960.

Weatherford, Elizabeth. "Women's Traditional Architecture." *Heresies: A Feminist Publication on Art and Politics,* Issue 2: "Patterns of Communication and the Use of Space," May 1977, pp. 35–39.

Weisman, Leslie Kanes. *Discrimination by Design: A Feminist Critique of the Man-made Environment.* Chicago: University of Chicago Press, 1992.

Werkerle, Gerda, Rebecca Peterson, and David Morley, eds. *New Space for Women.* Boulder, Colo.: Westview Press, 1981.

Wharton, Edith, and Ogden Codman, Jr. *The Decoration of Houses.* New York: W. W. Norton & Co., 1978 (1897).

Wigley, Mark. "Postmortem Architecture: A Taste of Derrida." *Perspecta,* Vol. 23, pp. 156–72.

———. "Untitled: The Housing of Gender." *Sexuality & Space.* Edited by Beatriz Colomina. New York: Princeton Architectural Press, 1992, pp. 326–89.

Wilson, Elizabeth. *The Sphinx in the City: Urban Life, the Control of Disorder, and Women.* Berkeley: University of California Press, 1991.

Wittkower, Rudolf. *Architectural Principles in the Age of Humanism.* New York: W. W. Norton & Company, 1971 (1961).

Wolf, Naomi. *The Beauty Myth: How Images of Beauty Are Used Against Women.* New York: Anchor Books, 1992 (1991).

Wright, Frank Lloyd. "The Art and Craft of the Machine." *Frank Lloyd Wright: Writings and Buildings.* Edited by Edgard Kaufmann and Ben Raeburn. New York: New American Library, 1974 (1905), pp. 55–73.

Wright, Gwendolyn. *Building the Dream: A Social History of Housing in America.* Cambridge, Mass.: MIT Press, 1983.

Illustration Credits

Introduction

I.1 Musées de la Ville de Paris © by SPADEM 1994; I.3 Collection Debuisson; I.4 courtesy of the Master and Fellows, Magdalene College, Cambridge; I.5 The Toledo Museum of Art, Florence Scott Libbey Bequest in memory of her father, Maurice A. Scott; I.6 ©1995 ARS, New York/SPADEM, Paris; I.7 Wurts; I.8 Musées de la Ville de Paris © by SPADEM 1994

Chapter 1

1.1 E. Guidoni, *Primitive Architecture* (Electa, 1975), based on J.-P. Lebeuf, *L'Habitation des Fali, montagnards du Cameroun septentrional: Technologie, sociologie, mythologie, symbolisme* (Paris: Hachette, 1961) and M. Griaule, *Masques Dogons* (Paris: Institut d'Ethnologie, 1938); 1.4–5 Photothèque du Musée de l'Homme, Paris; 1.6 G. Semper, *Der Stil in den technischen und tektonischen Künsten oder Praktische Ästhetik: Ein Handbuch für Techniker, Künstler und Kunstfreunde* (Munich, 1863); 1.7 G. Maxwell, *People of the Reeds* (New York: Harper, 1957); 1.8 M.-A. Laugier, *Essai sur l'architecture*, 2nd edition (Paris, 1755), Frontispiece

Chapter 2

2.1 Hirmer Verlag; 2.2 R. Koldewey, *Das Ischtar-tor in Babylon* (Leipzig, 1918); 2.3–4 J. Mellaart, *Çatal Hüyük: A Neolithic Town in Anatolia* (London: Thames and Hudson, 1967); 2.6 Frances Loeb Library, Harvard University; 2.7 Ente Nazionale Industrie Turistiche; 2.8 P. Lefèvre; 2.9 Electa Editrice; 2.10 S. Kostoff, *A History of Architecture* (Oxford University Press, 1985); 2.11 A. Alphand, *Les Promenades de Paris* (Paris, 1868–1873); 2.13 Carl W. Blegen and Marion Rawson, *The Palace of Nestor at Pylos in Western Messina*, Vol. I: *The Buildings and Their Contents*, Part 1, © 1966 by Princeton University Press, reprinted by permission of the publisher; 2.14 Electa Editrice; 2.15 Hirmer Verlag; 2.16 Greek National Tourist Office; 2.17 C. Praschniker, "Das Basisrelief der Parthenos," Jahreshefte des Osterreichischen Archäologischen Instituts, Vol. XXXIX, 1952, opposite p. 7; 2.18 M. Schede, *Die Ruinen von Priene: Kurze Beschreibung* (Berlin, 1964); 2.19 A. von Gerkan, *Griechische Städteanlagen* (Berlin, 1924) ; 2.20 Richard Tobias, based on reconstruction drawing by J. Ellis Jones; 2.21 Metropolitan Museum of Art, New York, Fletcher Fund, 1931; 2.22 National Gallery, London

Chapter 3

3.1 Richard Tobias, based on G. Fanelli, *Firenze* (Bari, 1980); 3.2 Gloucester City Museum, drawn by P. A. Moss; 3.3 R. Herzog et al., *Kos*, Vol. I: P. Schazmann, *Asklepieion* (Berlin, 1932) ; 3.4–5 British Architectural Library Photographs Collection; 3.6 courtesy of MacConnal-Mason Fine Paintings, London; 3.7 W. Jashemski, *The Gardens of Pompeii* (New York: Aristide D. Caratzas, 1994), reproduced courtesy of the publisher; 3.8 Pontificia Commissione di Archeologia Sacra, Rome; 3.9 Electa Editrice; 3.11 C. Connor, *Art and Miracles in Medieval Byzantium* (Princeton University Press, 1991); 3.12 D. Brabbs, *English Country Churches* (London: Weidenfeld and Nicolson, 1985), reprinted courtesy of the publisher; 3.13 Giraudon/Art Resource, NY; 3.14 A. Chatelain; 3.15 Musée Condé, Chantilly

Chapter 4

4.1 Charlemagne Exposition, Aix-la-Chapelle (1965); 4.2 Frances Loeb Library, Harvard University; 4.3 Electa Editrice; 4.4 J. van Remoortere, *Abbayes et Béguinages de Belgique* (Brussels, 1981); 4.5 Giraudon/Art Resource, NY; 4.6 Giraudon/Art Resource, NY; 4.7 Electa Editrice; 4.8 J. Ainaud and A. Held, *Romanesque Painting* (Amsterdam: J. M. Meulenhoff, 1963); 4.9 Musée Condé, Chantilly, Giraudon/Art Resource, NY; 4.10 British Library, London; 4.11 Service Photographique, Bibliotèque Nationale, Paris.; 4.12 Giraudon/Art Resource, NY; 4.13 National Gallery, London; 4.14 Alinari/Art Resource, NY

Chapter 5

5.1 Walters Art Gallery, Baltimore; 5.2 F. Hartt, *Italian Renaissance Art* (New York: Harry N. Abrams Inc., 1979); 5.3 Bildarchiv Preussischer Kulturbesitz, Berlin; 5.5 A. Pozzo, *Perspectivum pictorium et architectorum* (Rome, 1693–1702); 5.6 Accademia, Venice; 5.7 a) Biblioteca Laurenziana, Florence, b–c) Fra Giocondo, *M. Vitruvius per Jocundum* (Venice, 1511), d) F. Giorgi, *De Harmonia Mundi* (Venice, 1525) ; 5.8 Cesariano, *Lucio Vitruvio Pollione de Architectura* (Como, 1521); 5.9 Alinari/Art Resource, NY; 5.10 Foto Marburg/Art Resource, NY; 5.11 Alinari/Art Resource, NY; 5.12 author photograph; 5.13 M. Wundram, T. Pape, P. Marton, *Palladio* (Keulen: Benedikt Taschen Verlag, 1988); 5.14 Electa Editrice; 5.15 Alinari/Art Resource, NY; 5.16 Serlio, Book II (from 1551 ed., fols. 28–30); 5.17 Giraudon/Art Resource, NY; 5.18 Electa Editrice; 5.19 Giraudon/Art Resource, NY; 5.21 Courtesy of the Hermès Collection, Paris; 5.22 J.-N.-L. Durand, *Précis des Leçons d'Architecture données à L'École Polytechnique* (Paris, 1802); 5.23, 25, 26 C.-N. Ledoux, *L'Architecture considérée sous le rapport de l'art des moeurs et de la législation* (Paris, 1804); 5.24 *Visionary Architects: Boullée, Ledoux, Lequeu* (Houston: University of St. Thomas, 1968)

Chapter 6

6.1 The Netherlands Office for the Fine Arts, The Hague/Museum Boymans-van Beuningen, Rotterdam.; 6.2 Musée du Louvre, © Photo RMN; 6.3 Rijksmuseum, Amsterdam; 6.4 Staatliche Kunstsammlungen, Dresden; 6.5 Metropolitan Museum of Art, New York; 6.8 F. Kimball, *The Creation of the Rococo Decorative Style* (New York: Dover Publications, 1980); 6.9 Musée du Louvre, © photo RMN; 6.10 A. Blunt, *Baroque and Rococo, Architecture and Decoration* (New York: Harper and Row, 1978); 6.11 Alte Pinakothek, Munich; 6.12 A. Pope, *The Rape of the Lock* (1896), facing p. 6; 6.13 Giraudon/Art Resource, NY; 6.14 Victoria & Albert Museum, London/Art Resource, NY; 6.16 Giraudon/Art Resource, NY; 6.17 Sir John Soane's Museum, London; 6.18 Musée du Louvre, © photo RMN; 6.19 Musée du Louvre, © photo RMN

Chapter 7

7.1 photograph © 1994, The Art Institute of Chicago. All rights reserved; 7.2 Victoria & Albert Museum, London/Art Resource, NY; 7.3 Electa Editrice; 7.4 courtesy of Western Union; 7.5 Musée d'Orsay, Paris, © photo RMN; 7.6 Metropolitan Museum of Art, New York; 7.7 Popperprints, London; 7.8 Graphische Sammlung, Staatsgalerie, Stuttgart; 7.9 City of Bristol Museum and Art Gallery; 7.10 O. Jones, The Grammar of Ornament (London: Day and Son, 1856) ; 7.11 A.W.N. Pugin, *Contrasts; or, a Parallel Between the Noble Edifices of the Middle Ages, and Corresponding Buildings of the Present Day, Shewing the Present Decay of Taste* (London, 1841); 7.12 Victoria & Albert Museum, London/Art Resource, NY; 7.13 Chester Dale Fund, © 1994 Board of Trustees, National Gallery of Art, Washington; 7.14 The Brooklyn Museum , gift of Miss Gwendolyn O. L. Conkling; 7.15 *Artistic Houses* (New York, 1883), The Collection of American Literature, The Beinecke Rare Book and Manuscript Library, Yale University; 7.16 E. Howard, *Garden Cities of Tomorrow* (1902); 7.17 R. Unwin, *Town Planning in Practice* (1909); 7.18 photograph © 1994, The Art Institute of Chicago. All rights reserved; 7.19 Reilly and Constantine Commercial, Birmingham; 7.20 Chevojon Frères, Paris

Chapter 8

8.1–3 courtesy Harriet Beecher Stowe Center, Hartford; 8.4 E. Lupton, *Mechanical Brides: Women and Machines from the Home to the Office* (Princeton Architectural Press, 1993); 8.5 Photograph courtesy of the Museum of Modern Art, New York; 8.6 courtesy of the Musée d'Art Moderne, Strasbourg; 8.7 Rijksdienst Beeldende Kunst, The Hague; 8.9 Bauhaus-Archiv, © Stölzl: Beeldrecht,Amsterdam; 8.10–11 Centraal Museum, Utrecht; 8.12 Grant Mudford; 8.14 still from *L'Architecture d'aujourd'hui* (1929); 8.15 ©1995 ARS, New York/SPADEM, Paris; 8.16 Photograph © 1994 The Museum of Modern Art, New York, Nelson A. Rockefeller Bequest; 8.17 Musée Picasso, Paris, © Photo RMN-SPADEM; 8.18 Sprengel Museum, Hannover; 8.19 Graphische Sammlung Albertina, Vienna; 8.20 William Allin Storrer, *The Frank Lloyd Wright Companion* (University of Chicago Press, 1993); 8.21 Peter Christian Haberkorn; 8.22 author photograph; 8.23 E. Wharton and O. Codman, Jr., *The Decoration of Houses* (New York: W. W. Norton & Co., 1978); 8.24 courtesy Michael Graves; 8.25–26 Aaron Spelling Productions

ILLUSTRATION CREDITS

Chapter 9
9.1 R. Chelminski, Paris (Amsterdam: Time-
Life International, 1977) ; 9.2 D. Hayden,
"What Would a Non-Sexist City Be Like? Spec-
ulations on Housing, Urban Design, and
Human Work," in C. R. Stimpson, ed., *Women
and the American City* (Chicago, 1980); 9.3
courtesy Peter Calthorpe Associates; 9.5
Collection of the Museum of Contemporary
Art, Chicago, gift of Mr. and Mrs. E. A.
Bergman and Susan and Lewis Manilow; 9.6,
9.9 Esto Photographics; 9.7, 9.10 courtesy
Frank O. Gehry and Associates; 9.8 Yale University Art Gallery, Gift of the Société
Anonyme; 9.11–13 courtesy Diller +
Scofidio; 9.14 photo: Margherita Krischanitz;
9.15 courtesy Henry Dreyfuss Associates,
New York; 9.16 courtesy Eisenman Architects; 9.17 courtesy Coop Himmelblau;
9.18–20 courtesy Lebbeus Woods; 9.21 ©
1986 Twentieth Century Fox Film Corp.;
9.22 courtesy Rosanna Liebman